Read 104 – 109

D0346035

Books of related interest published by Stanley Thornes:

Brain & Martin: *Child Care and Health for Nursery Nurses* 3rd edn, 1990.
Hobart & Frankel: *A Practical Guide to Working with Young Children*
Stoyle: *Caring for Older People*

A First Course in Caring

Liam Clarke
Karen Rowell
Margaret White

Stanley Thornes (Publishers) Ltd

The illustrations of Health Education Authority material shown on pages 59, 64, 69, 83, 92 and 95–7 are reproduced courtesy of the Health Education Authority.

First published in 1992 by:
Stanley Thornes (Publishers) Ltd
Old Station Drive
Leckhampton
CHELTENHAM GL53 0DN
England

Reprinted 1993

British Library Cataloguing in Publication Data

A catalogue for this book is available from the British Library.

ISBN 0–7487–1509–6

Typeset by Tech-Set, Gateshead, Tyne & Wear
Printed and bound in Great Britain at The Bath Press, Avon

Contents

Introduction

Over the past five years new caring courses and vocational qualifications have been developed for those professionals working in the health and social care field.

This book is primarily aimed at students in schools and colleges who are following a foundation level programme of study, particularly the BTEC First Award in Caring, it is also a useful source book for students taking First Level City & Guilds courses in care.

As a source of reference, this book will be useful for those who are employed in the caring field and who are working towards the attainment of a NVQ at Level 2. It covers the underpinning knowledge necessary for students to gain NVQs in Health and Social Care and obtain a foundation qualification in Caring. In preparing the text, developments relating to the Integration Project and the introduction of General National Vocational Qualifications (GNVQs) have been taken into account as far as possible.

The book's emphasis is on active learning with activities and assignments for the students to complete. How the book is used will, to some extent, be determined by the organisation of the course you are attending. However, you should read and carry out the activities and assignments in Chapter 7 early on in your course of study. This will enable you to gain the investigative skills necessary to obtain the maximum benefit from the content of the other chapters. Chapter 8 on work placement could be worked through during the induction period of the programme of study.

Acknowledgements

We cannot mention individually everyone with whom we discussed ideas which led to the writing of this book, but a special thanks must go to the many students who over the years have shared their ideas and values with us. We acknowledge the debt that we owe those students.

The authors also wish to thank Eileen Brown for her valuable contribution on diet in Chapter 4.

Dr Liam Clarke PhD, BA (Law), CSW, has worked as a senior manager in Social Service Departments before entering the social work teaching profession in 1980. He has advised BTEC on the development of social care courses for a number of years and is at present a moderator for BTEC courses and External Verifier for BTEC and City and Guilds NVQ schemes. He is the Programme Manager for the Health and Social Care Programme at Norton College.

Karen Rowell BEd, is the Course manager for the BTEC National Diploma in Caring Services (Social Care) at Norton College.

Margaret White RGN, OHN Cert, Cert Ed, has worked in the health service for a number of years. She is at present the Course Manager for the BTEC in Caring First Award at Norton College.

Caring skills

AIMS

▶ To consider the practical, social and psychological skills necessary to enable you to operate effectively in the caring environment.

▶ To understand the importance of hygiene, health and safety in the working environment, and how to prevent infection spreading.

▶ To be aware of the specialist aids, appliances and equipment available.

▶ To learn the correct techniques for moving and handling clients.

▶ To observe and understand the physical and psychological needs of clients.

▶ To learn how to cope with death and help with bereavement and grieving.

A CARING ATTITUDE

You have chosen to work in social care because you feel that you have a caring personality and want to help people. Perhaps your most important assets are your personality and your attitude towards the people you are caring for.

ACTIVITY

Look at these examples.

Decide how you would feel in the two situations if you were the older person sitting in the chair.

As we grow older our own experiences of life help us to understand more about some of the problems the people we are looking after face. As a young 'carer' you will want to consider some of the attributes you will need in your chosen career.

Your attitude is most important. The people you will be working with will all be experiencing difficulties of some sort. For example, they may have no control over movement, they be unable to speak or may have impaired sight or hearing.

In college you are the focus of attention of the staff, but in work-experience placement you become part of the caring team, focusing attention on the clients (the people you are caring for).

ACTIVITY

Take a partner and ask them to assist you to blow your nose (use clean, disposable tissues only).

1 How does it feel to be dependent on another person?

2 Discuss your feelings with the rest of your group.

3 Discuss situations when a client might find dependence upsetting.

In order to help clients in a sensitive and caring manner remember to pay constant attention to the effectiveness of your communication skills. Be polite and respectful, speaking to clients and co-workers in a clear voice.

All caring work involves good interpersonal skills. Talk to the client about what you are doing. This will help them to feel at ease as they will understand what you are doing and the reasons for your actions. Many of the tasks you will carry out will be of a practical nature, but never forget to maintain a friendly, welcoming approach, and always show an interest and understanding of your clients' individual needs. Try to be helpful and supportive – be ready to respond with conversation, a laugh, a smile or a word of comfort. Your clients will also derive comfort from touch, so hold their hands, put an arm round their shoulders or give them a cuddle.

Aim to:

- Listen and respond to communications from clients and co-workers.
- Use good eye contact and keep smiling.
- Be sincere, sympathetic and understanding.
- Be kind, gentle and tactful.
- Be willing to assist, but always remember to allow your clients to do as much as possible for themselves. Encourage them to be as independent as is practical.

SPECIAL WORDS

As with any area of work there is a whole new vocabulary to understand.

Look carefully at the following list of terms:

- congenital
- mental handicap
- physical disability
- pre-school child
- rising fives
- pre-term baby
- neo-natal
- geriatric
- psycho-geriatric
- multi-cultural
- psychological
- paediatric.

1 Discuss with your colleagues their meanings.

2 As a group produce a dictionary which could be used by future students going into work experience.

Remember to make your list alphabetical. How about using the word processor or even illustrations? You will be able to add to your list during the course.

Some of your work experience may involve working in hospitals. Perhaps you have noticed those rather large signposts outside your local hospital and wondered what all the names mean.

ACTIVITY

1 Following discussion within your group, make a list of all the ward or department names with an explanation as to their functions.

2 Note if there are any instances where the information is translated into other languages.

3 If there are no translations, do you think there are any groups in the local community who may be disadvantaged by this omission?

CARING FOR DIFFERENT CLIENT GROUPS

The work you do will be in a variety of settings such as residential homes, hospitals, nurseries, creches, people's own homes, day centres, schools, special needs schools and various establishments for adults with special needs.

Outlined below are some examples of the practical tasks you will be expected to carry out in caring for various client groups.

The elderly

When working with elderly people you may be expected to carry out some or all of the following practical tasks:

- stripping, cleaning and making beds;
- dressing and undressing clients;
- helping clients to get in and out of bed;
- washing clients;
- attending to oral hygiene and dentures;
- hair care and shaving;
- washing clients' hands and caring for nails;
- helping clients to attend to personal laundry;
- taking clients to the toilet and assisting when necessary;
- assisting with mobility, the use of frames, wheelchairs and other aids;
- assisting with meals and feeding when necessary;
- reading to, and writing letters for, clients;
- playing games with clients;
- shopping with, or for, clients;
- caring for clients' clothing;
- routine tidying and dusting.

▲ *Shaving is one practical task you will be expected to carry out*

© Sam Tanner, courtesy of Age Concern England

In addition you will have to learn moving and handling techniques which will put less strain on you physically and cause the minimum discomfort to clients.

Children

When working with children you will need to develop a consistent approach and positive attitudes. Practical tasks in child-care situations include the following:

- observing activities;
- attending to toilet needs according to age;
- physical care of babies and young children;
- assisting with meals and feeding where necessary;
- helping with games and reading;
- setting up and clearing away toys and materials for play activities;
- involving children in imaginative play;
- directing children in safe play;
- assisting with outings and visits.

People with a physical or mental handicap

Working with people who have a mental or physical handicap may involve you in the following:

- preparing and serving meals;
- assisting with feeding;
- playing games;
- assisting with educational activities;
- assisting with visits and outings;
- helping with dressing and undressing;
- assisting clients with general physical care;
- assisting clients with their toilet needs;
- using aids and appliances to help clients;
- assisting clients with work or creative activities.

You will have noticed that many of the tasks in the above lists are applicable to different groups. For example, a baby may require a nappy change whereas an elderly person may need assistance with continence. This will be discussed later in this chapter. Always try to look beyond the disability and the task to the person you are dealing with. Your sensitivity to their needs is a fundamental part of caring.

ACTIVITY

1 Are the tasks listed above the sort you thought you would be involved in?

2 Did you realise the impact of attitude and communication skills on all aspects of caring?

CARRYING OUT THE TASKS INVOLVED IN CARING

In order to work effectively you need to have a system or a set of guidelines to work to. One way of setting up a system is to use the headings shown below.

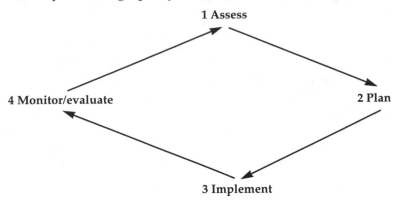

1 Assess the situation

In consultation with other staff find out exactly what needs to be done for the client. Before you decide what to do for your client, make sure that you are familiar with his or her preferences. Nothing should be decided without full consultation with your client and/or relatives.

2 Plan

Decide exactly what you will do. Make sure that all the equipment you will need is available and that help and advice have been sought if necessary.

3 Implement

Carry out the task fully. Do what you have planned.

4 Monitor and evaluate

Monitor and evaluate what you have done and decide if any modifications need to be made to make the procedure more effective the next time it is carried out.

ACTIVITY

1 How might you help people to help themselves in the following situations? Remember to think about your approach and take into consideration the client's feelings.

2 How would you talk to or approach the client in each case?

- A five-year-old child needs help tying his shoe laces.
- An 80-year-old woman is able to walk, but has difficulty when getting up from the sitting position. How can you assist her to use the lavatory?
- A blind person is about to eat a meal.
- A fellow student in college is confined to a wheelchair and wishes to use the lift.
- A four-year-old in an infant school wants to paint a picture.

CARING CAN BE HARD WORK

Inevitably, the caring role can give rise to difficult situations for both client and carer. Some of the more relevant situations are discussed below. Perhaps you can think of other issues which may arise?

Working with people is seldom an easy option. You may often feel:

- overworked and so have no time to listen to clients;
- your personal problems are affecting your work and attitude towards your clients;
- tired and impatient;
- immature and unable to understand a client's problem;
- difficulty in forming relationships with clients or co-workers;
- worried because the demands of your job are excessive;
- overwhelmed with paperwork.

Sometimes you may feel overwhelmed by the responsibilities and tasks you are expected to carry out. At times like this try to talk things over with colleagues and your supervisor.

ACTIVITY

Within your group discuss how you could help and support clients in the situations described below.

1 A client who is confused and totally dependent on the carer may:
   - feel restricted by the routine of the establishment;
   - miss his home and family;
   - be upset at being unable to keep personal possessions;
   - be unused to the establishment's food;
   - feel he has lost friends, independence and freedom.

2 A three-year-old child leaving her mother to attend a nursery or creche for the first time may:
   - miss her family;
   - be unable to express her needs to carers;
   - feel surrounded by strangers;
   - feel confused in an unfamiliar environment;
   - not be fully aware of events.

THE WORKING ENVIRONMENT

A pleasant environment for people who are ill or in care is essential as it will make them feel better. Carers will also feel more motivated if their working conditions are agreeable. Buildings and grounds should be well-maintained and attractive. Decorations in buildings need careful planning so that certain areas look bright, cheerful and stimulating while others are quiet and restful. In residential centres, a room where clients can entertain their friends and family away from other residents should always be available. Clients' wishes regarding these matters should be considered and their views taken seriously. Wherever possible, clients should have their own rooms and be offered choices in the furnishings and fittings.

Good, hygienic practices will make for a much more pleasing environment and will reduce the risk of infections spreading. In your work placement read the basic guidelines relating to hygiene and any health and safety rules that must be enforced.

Ventilation

Adequate ventilation is very important in order to ensure that the air which is being breathed is stimulating and refreshing for clients and staff. No doubt we have all experienced rooms where conditions are less than perfect, where there is a stuffy atmosphere, making you feel tired and causing headaches and other minor ailments. Windows should be opened to allow cross-ventilation. Visits to places of interest and outdoor activities can also be very beneficial to clients.

Household cleanliness

Much of this will be the responsibility of the domestic staff, but it is up to the carer to see that standards are maintained while a service is being offered. This will involve mopping up spills and wiping work surfaces, tables and chairs as required. Proprietary cleaners in the correct dilution should be used. Special care will need to be taken with items which are upholstered, such as chairs and mattresses.

Hand basins, baths, showers and bidets

These should all be cleaned at least once every 24 hours by domestic staff using a proprietary cleaner, hot water and clean or disposable cloths. Should equipment become soiled, day or night, it is up to carers to see that it is clean and ready again for clients' use.

Bed pans, potties and commodes

Scrupulous, routine cleaning is vital and all should be emptied immediately following use. You will find that different establishments use a variety of cleaning agents, including bleach solutions. Check the health and safety regulations in the work place before you use these cleaning materials. Disposable cloths are ideal for this type of cleaning. Hospitals and some larger establishments will use disposable bed pans and urinals. They may also require that different forms of waste be disposed of in separate containers.

Important points to remember
- Always were protective clothing when in contact with body fluids or waste of any kind.
- Always dispose of waste matter carefully, using the appropriate containers. Make sure you have instructions from your supervisor about this.
- Never leave cleaning materials where clients, especially small children, can reach them.
- Protect yourself by reading the instructions on labels of cleaning agents that you use and avoid coming into contact with them by using gloves and overalls or aprons.

Bedclothes and clients' clothing

Most large establishments will have laundry facilities or will contract out any laundry work. Carers' main responsibilities are to remove bedclothes and soiled clothing, and prepare them as required for the laundry.

Points to remember

- Bedding and clothing must be changed as soon as soiling occurs.
- Remove any excreta which is on the bedding or clothing. Do not forget to use gloves. Place items in special coloured bags, as directed by your supervisor, before sending them to the laundry. Placement supervisors will explain more about this.
- Small or delicate items should be hand washed for individual clients. Sometimes relatives will do this for the client.

Food preparation areas

In order to avoid food poisoning, areas where food is prepared in the various caring establishments need to be kept scrupulously clean and tidy. This responsibility is shared between carers and domestic staff. All work surfaces must be wiped frequently; bleach solutions are appropriate for this.

Play equipment, toys and games

Regular, thorough cleaning using household cleaners and sometimes weak solutions of bleach is essential for this type of equipment. Placement supervisors will give exact instructions.

ACTIVITY

1 In your work place, identify all the domestic tasks which are shared between domestic staff and carers. A list will probably be the clearest way of giving this information.

2 In relation to domestic tasks, examine one area where domestic work is particularly important. Prepare this information and report back to your group.

3 Within your group, discuss the importance of co-operation between all members of staff within caring establishments.

USING SPECIALIST AIDS, APPLIANCES AND EQUIPMENT

In your work placement you may use a number of aids and pieces of specialist equipment.

Aids to mobility

The aim of any care plan is always to encourage the clients to be as independent as possible within the limits of the conditions from which they are suffering. Allow clients to do as much as they can for themselves.

There are a wide variety of aids which enable the client with mobility problems to move around. They range from an electronically-controlled wheelchair to a simple walking stick. Clients will have been advised by medical staff, occupational therapists and physiotherapists as to the most appropriate help for them.

Wheelchairs

These may be electronically-controlled, hand-propelled by the client or pushed by a helper. Various accessories are available including trays, soft seats, safety straps and spring lifter seats. The amount of help a wheelchair user will need will obviously depend on the type of client involved. Remember that the aim is to encourage mobility as far as possible. Never take over if a client wants to try to move unaided.

▲ *An electronically-controlled wheelchair*   *Photograph courtesy of Age Concern England*

The steps which may be used when assisting clients in wheelchairs are as follows:

- Assess the situation and decide what is going to be required.
- Explain to the client what is going to happen.
- Look at the chair carefully to establish the position of the brake, the foot rests, the arm rests and any safety straps.
- Always ensure that the user is comfortably and, more importantly, safely seated.
- Make sure that arms and legs are positioned carefully in order to avoid knocks on doorways and other obstacles.
- When negotiating steps and kerbs, place your foot on the tipping lever, hold the chair firmly and tip it back to go up.
- Lower the chair down the kerb; the back wheels should touch the ground at the same time.
- If you are pushing a wheelchair, never go too quickly as this can be frightening for the client.
- When transferring clients to and from wheelchairs, make sure the brakes are firmly applied, footrests are turned out of the way, small front wheels are turned inwards and the appropriate arm of the chair is removed.

Within your group take turns to spend an hour in a wheelchair being pushed to classes and around the building.

Produce a written account of your feelings. Present your account to the rest of the group.

Hoists

These are devices which enable carers to move clients gently and safely from one place to another. Many different types are available; some are electrically-powered and some are manually-operated. Usually there is some kind of sling in which the client is supported, attached to the hoist by metal hooks. The client is then moved in the sling either mechanically or manually, depending upon the type of hoist. As a student you will only be allowed to observe the use of hoists.

Lifts

Some homes for the elderly and disabled are fitted with stairlifts. These allow clients to move from different levels easily and safely, but carers should help and supervise their use.

Walking sticks

For people who need extra support when walking, a variety of sticks are available (see Figure 1.1). They are usually made from aluminium and can be adjusted in length or folded. Variations include tripod and quadruped sticks which provide extra stability, and traditional, wooden sticks are still popular. Seat sticks are useful, being made of light-weight aluminium and can be turned into a seat when the user wants to rest for short periods.

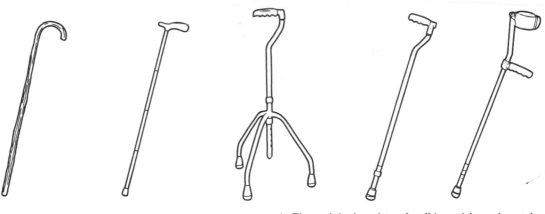

▲ Figure 1.1 A variety of walking sticks and crutches

Crutches

For people who are unable to bear their own weight or who need extra support when walking, a range of light-weight, aluminium elbow crutches are available. Their height can be adjusted to suit the individual. It is important that clients and carers should understand the correct way to use crutches and a physiotherapist will usually advise on this.

Walking frames

The best known walking frame is the *Zimmer*. Frames give good support enabling clients to stand or walk safely.

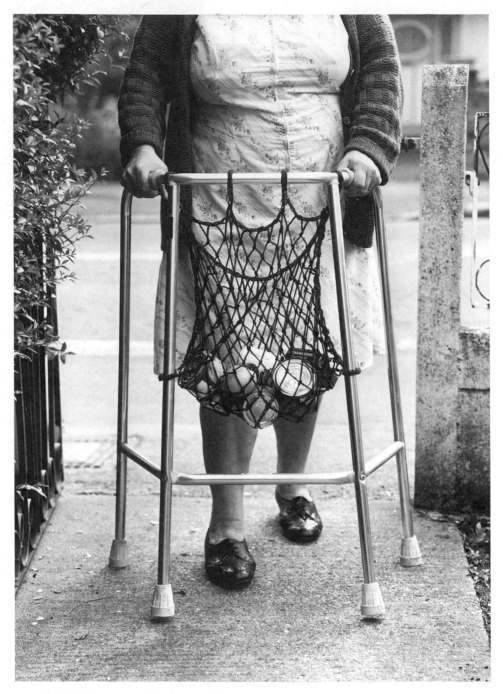

▲ *The Zimmer frame*   © *Barry Shapcott, courtesy of Age Concern England*

Adjustable walkers with wheels

These aids to mobility are made from steel and usually have two fixed wheels at the front and two rubber feet at the back. They can be adjusted in height so that the user can rest their arms on the frame.

Bed comfort

Although clients are encouraged to get up and to be as mobile as possible there will always be situations where they spend considerable periods of time in bed or sitting in a chair. Comfort can be improved (see Figure 1.2) by using:

- pillows to give extra support (triangular-shaped pillows are often used);
- backrests to give support when sitting upright in bed;
- bed cradles to protect or take the weight of bed clothes;
- rings and cushions to sit on;
- fleecy pads to protect buttocks, elbows and heels;
- ladder hoists which consist of a simple arrangement allowing clients to pull themselves into a sitting position when in bed or in the bath;
- trapeze lifts to help clients to move in bed or in the bath.

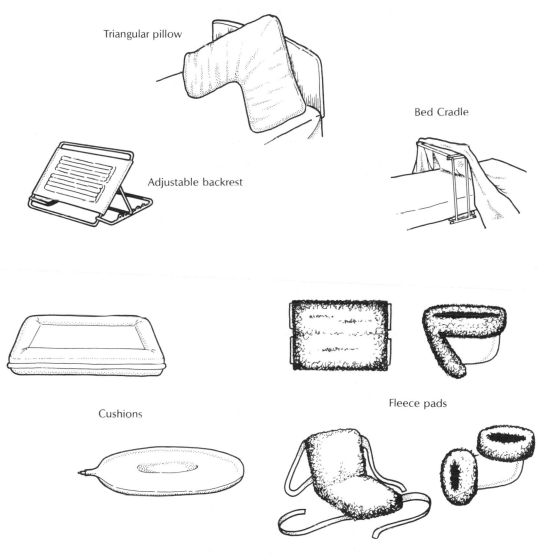

Triangular pillow

Bed Cradle

Adjustable backrest

Cushions

Fleece pads

▲ *Figure 1.2 Aids to provide bed comfort*

Remember that as a learner you would not use any of these items without help and advice from your supervisor.

Bathroom aids

A vast array of equipment is available to assist clients and carers with washing and bathing (see Figure 1.3). Examples include:

- special showers and baths;
- safety rails;
- bath seats;
- mobile shower chairs;
- grip bath and shower mats.

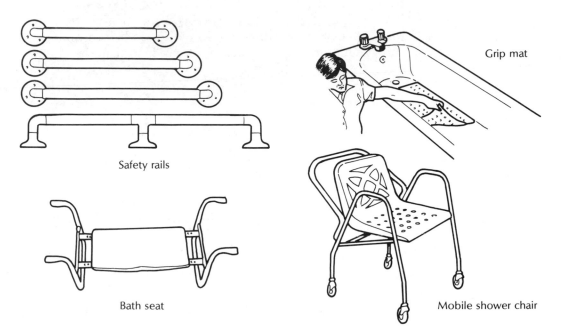

Grip mat

Safety rails

Bath seat

Mobile shower chair

▲ *Figure 1.3 Bathroom aids*

Toilet aids

When clients are confined to bed then bed pans and urinals may have to be used. This is not ideal and whenever possible the client should be taken to the lavatory or use a commode. Equipment available includes:

- special toilet seats;
- raised seats;
- inflatable toilet seats;
- sanichairs.

Aids to help with eating and drinking

Many disabled and elderly people you will meet during your work experience are helped to maintain independence when eating and drinking using a variety of devices including:

- special cutlery;
- feeding cups;
- plate guards;
- automatic feeders.

In addition, there are many devices to assist in the kitchen, such as tin openers, tap turners, potato peelers and twister bottle openers.

In general, there is a wide variety of aids and equipment available which will cater for almost any disability.

ACTIVITY

In your home area there is probably a supplier of aids and appliances for disabled people. Either visit the supplier's showroom or request that a product catalogue be sent to you.

Choose *one* of the following situations:

- a young man is paralysed and confined to a wheelchair;
- an elderly person is deaf and only able to walk with assistance;
- an elderly lady is suffering from arthritis in her hands and experiences difficulty with manipulative skills.
- an eight-year-old child is very overweight and is unable to stand or walk without assistance.

1 Make a list of all the aids and appliances which would assist the person in the situation you have chosen.

2 Explain carefully the function of each item you have listed.

3 Write down the price of each item you have listed.

4 Work out the total cost of all the items.

5 Find out what financial assistance is available for people who need to purchase items to support them in everyday situations.

MOBILITY, MOVING AND HANDLING TECHNIQUES

Movement, or assisting with movement, of clients frequently becomes the responsibility of the carer. Since back problems can occur when moving and handling clients it is very important that potential carers learn the techniques involved.

Working safely when moving and handling clients

Your back allows you to do everything from sleeping to mountain climbing. People who experience back problems suffer pain and often have to take time off work. This can result in diminished earnings, inconvenience and even permanent disability.

Did you know that:

- At some time in their lives four out of five people will suffer from back pain.
- 24 million working days are lost each year at a cost of over £1 billion per annum.
- Approximately five per cent of people have to change the nature of their work completely because of back problems.

Back pain and problems can be caused by:

- sprains due to faulty lifting;
- disc trouble;
- poor posture;
- lack of exercise;
- being overweight;
- injuries;
- diseases.

You can help yourself avoid back problems by ensuring that you maintain a good posture and making sure that you rest your muscles when you stand, sit and sleep.

Follow these simple rules:

stand correctly with –
- your head high
- your chin in
- your chest forward
- your abdomen flat.

sit correctly with –
- your knees higher than your hips
- your lower back firm against the backrest.

sleep correctly with –
- a firm mattress
- a bed board
- your knees bent and lying on your side.

Before lifting:
- Assess the situation first.
- Know when to get help and advice.
- Predict potential difficulties.
- Follow the rules and methods your supervisors have explained.
- Use new and improved methods and equipment, and keep up to date with developments.

General rules when lifting any object:
- Think.
- Examine the object.
- Clear the immediate area.
- Know how and where to position the item to be lifted.
- Get help if necessary.
- Stand close, with a firm footing and feet apart (Step 1 of Figure 1.4).
- Straddle the object, keeping a straight back and bend the knees (Step 2 of Figure 1.4).
- Grasp the item firmly to prevent slipping (Step 3 of Figure 1.4).
- Breathe in, as inflated lungs support the spine.
- Slowly straighten your legs, bringing them back to the vertical position (Step 4 of Figure 1.4).
- Hold the item firmly and close to the body (Step 5 of Figure 1.5).
- Avoid sudden, jerky movements.
- Lift with a smooth action.
- Turn your feet **not** your back.

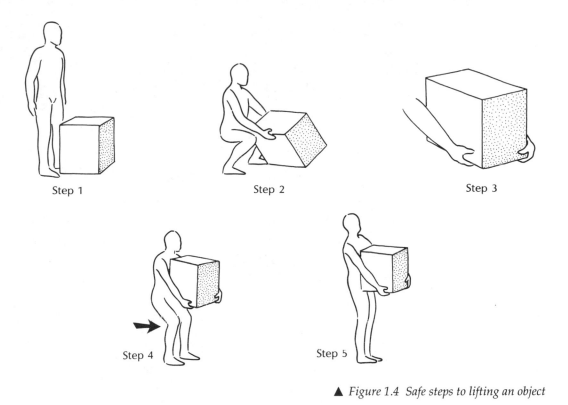

Step 1   Step 2   Step 3

Step 4   Step 5

▲ *Figure 1.4 Safe steps to lifting an object*

Lifting or moving a client

When lifting or moving a client some specific rules apply:

- Always wear flat shoes.
- It is advisable to remove rings and watches. These may scratch the client or get caught in hair.
- Explain the procedure to the person who is being lifted.
- Clear the area.
- Where there is more than one lifter co-operate to lift in unison.
- Do not rush the procedure.
- Do not drag the client.
- Apply all the general rules of lifting.

When you are in the work place, procedures will have been drawn up which you must follow.

Remember!

Always follow the rules.

Helping clients with dressing and undressing

In your work, you may have to help your clients to dress and undress. This may sound straightforward, but the type of clothes we wear and the reasons we wear them can be very significant.

▲ *Dressing a client*   © *Sam Tanner, courtesy of Age Concern England*

We wear clothes for warmth, protection and to look good, or to denote religious or cultural groups or professional identity. Some people may find it a disturbing experience if they are unable to follow their usual style of dressing.

In order to maintain both physical and psychological comfort, you should aim to dress the client as closely to his or her normal style as possible. Before you start look at the following check list of questions to consider:

- What can I learn about the client from his or her clothes?
- Are there any specific religious observances that I need to know about?
- What age is the client?
- Does he or she follow fashion trends closely?
- What are their special likes and dislikes?
- Will frequent changes of clothing be necessary?
- Is special clothing necessary in cases of incontinence?
- Is the client able to cope with fastenings?
- What time of year is it?
- Is protective clothing required to allow the client to indulge in various activities?

Try to encourage clients to do as much as they can for themselves. It makes them feel better and encourages independence.

When clients are in some form of residential care they should retain their own clothes and be involved in choosing what they would like to wear. Carers must know about the aids available to assist with dressing and undressing, and be able to demonstrate their uses to clients. It is also very important to ensure that clothing is clean and changed when necessary.

OBSERVATION OF CLIENTS

Carers need to acquire the skill of being observant. Before we can care for a client effectively we must be able to assess their needs so that we can plan for their care. Assessment will be based on the observations carers have made and the information clients and relatives give. This observation is both *physical* and *psychological*.

Here is a list of some of the observations carers should make during their day-to-day care of clients:

- Is the client happy, sad, bored or dejected?
- What is the client's attitude to other people and his or her surroundings?
- How mobile is the client?
- Is the client anxious or tense?
- Can the client see?
- Can the client hear?
- Can the client smell and taste?
- Can the client talk or are non-verbal methods of communication used?
- Is the client clean? Is there any body odour?
- Does the client suffer from halitosis?
- Does the client have a good appetite? Are there any difficulties with eating and drinking?
- Does the client suffer from excessive thirst?
- Does the client have dentures?
- Is the client mentally alert?
- Does the client exhibit any abnormal behaviour patterns?
- What is the state of the client's skin? Are there any spots, rashes or pressure sores?
- Is the client incontinent?
- Is the client in any pain?
- Are there any abnormalities in urine, faeces or sputum?

More specific observations of temperature, pulse, respiration and urine may be required.

Taking temperatures

The normal body temperature is between 36 °C and 37 °C. Even when the environmental temperature changes significantly a human's body temperature will stay constant. A healthy adult will manage to maintain body temperature by balancing heat loss from the skin with types of food eaten and clothing worn.

Problems arise when the balance between heat loss and heat gain are disturbed. The body's response to infection is a rise in temperature above 37 °C; this state is known as *pyrexia*. If, on the other hand, the body loses more heat than can be produced and the temperature falls below 35 °C then *hypothermia* results.

40 °C or above is considered a dangerously high body temperature and a dangerously low temperature is 35 °C and below. There are four main types of thermometer available to record body temperature. These are:

- clinical thermometers;
- digital thermometers;
- disposable thermometers;
- forehead thermometers.

The type of thermometer used will depend upon the circumstances and degree of accuracy required.

A thermometer should never be placed in the mouth, in the following situations:

- where the client is unconscious;
- where the client is a baby or small child;
- where the client suffers from fits;
- where the client is confused;
- where the client has injuries to, or infection of, the mouth.

When taking temperatures, follow the instructions which are specific to the type of thermometer which is being used. Note the temperature carefully as excessively high or low temperatures must be brought immediately to the attention of the supervisor or carer who is in charge.

Hypothermia in an elderly person

The body temperature can fall below normal, bringing about a sleepy state which can lead to death. Elderly people who live alone are prone to suffer from hypothermia.

Signs of hypothermia include:

- drowsiness
- slurred speech
- pale, cold skin
- unsteady movements
- slow, shallow breathing.

In addition, the body temperature will be 35 °C or below and a special, low-reading thermometer will be needed to check this.

Hypothermia is a very serious situation and medical help should be summoned. Meanwhile, the elderly person should be wrapped in blankets and given a warm drink, and the room should be warmed.

Many organisations, including Help the Aged, Age Concern, local authorities and gas and electricity companies, give help and advice on the prevention of hypothermia in elderly people.

1 Collect as much information as you can from the various sources available in your locality.

2 Write a concise report of your findings.

Hypothermia in a newborn baby

Until the heat-regulating mechanism of the brain is fully developed a baby relies on the temperature of his or her surroundings to maintain body temperature. If a room seems cold to you then it is certainly far too cold for a baby. A baby who is suffering from hypothermia may actually have quite rosy cheeks, but the skin will fell very cold. Typically, such a baby will be lethargic, immobile, unresponsive and will not feed. Urgent medical help is required in this situation. Meanwhile, warm the room and wrap the baby to warm gradually.

Note that:

- Large amounts of heat are lost from the head. Therefore, the head should be covered to restrict this heat loss.
- Elderly people may have thin hair or be bald. This is often also the case with babies, but in addition the head of a baby is large in proportion to the body.
- Special room thermometers are available for use in the homes of elderly people or babies' bedrooms.

How do you help clients who have a high temperature?

The aim is to prevent the temperature from rising to a dangerously-high level. Cool drinks should be given, and excessive clothing and bed clothes should be removed. Sometimes the client may be sponged with tepid water or an electric fan may be used.

Taking pulses

Each time the heart beats to pump blood into the circulation, a wave passes along the walls of the arteries. This wave is the pulse and it can be felt at any point in the body where a large artery crosses a bone just beneath the skin. The pulse is usually counted at the *radial artery* in the wrist or the *carotid artery* in the neck.

Counting the pulse

The finger tips are placed over the site where the pulse is being taken. The beats are counted for a full minute and then recorded. The three main observations which are made on the pulse are:

- rate
- rhythm
- strength.

The average adult pulse rate varies between 60 and 80 beats per minutes, whereas a young baby has a pulse rate of about 140 beats per minute. Normally the rhythm is regular and the volume is sufficient to make the pulse easily felt. An increased pulse rate may indicate recent exercise, emotion or stress, infection, blood or fluid loss, shock or heart disease.

Practise taking the pulse rates of your colleagues.

1 Make an accurate recording of each group member's pulse rate.

2 Calculate the average pulse rate for your particular group.

PREVENTING THE SPREAD OF INFECTION

The word 'infection' means the passing of disease from one source to another. Infection spreads from one source to another in a variety of ways from:

- droplets or dust in the air;
- skin and mucus membranes;
- wounds;
- food and drink;
- soil;
- animals;
- infected articles.

Infections are caused by *microbes* (small living organisms). The main groups of microbes which are involved in the infective process are bacteria, viruses, fungi and protozoa.

Find out about, and make lists of, diseases caused by:

- bacteria
- viruses
- fungi
- protozoa.

When working in a caring environment, carers should know how to prevent infection from spreading. The body has certain defences which protect against infection as shown in Figure 1.5.

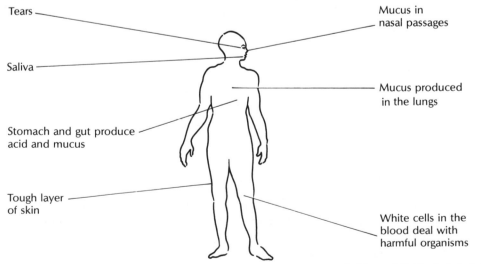

▲ *Figure 1.5 The body's defences*

The following is a list of some of the ways in which the spread of infection can be prevented:

- educating everybody in its prevention;
- adopting high standards of personal hygiene;
- enforcing high standards of food hygiene;
- providing good-quality accommodation;
- adopting high standards of sanitation, including facilities for washing hands;
- disinfecting or burning articles used by infected persons;
- avoiding contact with infected people;
- ensuring good ventilation;
- reporting all infective illnesses immediately;
- making sure the establishment is clean throughout.

ACTIVITY

1 In your work placement look round and check out the measures taken to prevent the spread of infection.

2 Compare those you have seen with the list above.

Some simple routines to prevent the spread of infection are outlined below.

Avoiding contact with blood and body fluids

Always wear plastic gloves when in contact with blood or body fluids. If you are in contact with such matter, wash your hands thoroughly with soap and water.

Avoiding contact with cuts and abrasions

Cover open wounds with waterproof dressings. Blue plasters should always be provided for food handlers.

Disinfecting

Wear plastic gloves and an apron when mopping up. Disinfect areas contaminated by blood and excreta with bleach solution. Dispose of contaminated waste by using the appropriate bags and containers.

> **Remember, good hygiene prevents the spread of infection**

ACTIVITY

You are working in a food preparation area and cut your finger with a knife. The finger bleeds.

What should you do? Describe the steps.

DEATH AND BEREAVEMENT

Death can occur in clients of any age. It can be distressing for carers, particularly when it is untimely. Death can be sudden, as in the case of an acute heart attack, or expected, for example at the end of a long illness.

Carers have an important role in ensuring that clients who are dying have a dignified and peaceful death, and that relatives are given support in their grief.

The person who is dying should be as comfortable and free from pain as possible. Carers will need to give emotional support and be prepared to be totally responsive to the client's needs.

As death approaches certain signs will be present; the pulse will be weak, there may be signs of blueness and breathing difficulties.

After death has occurred, special care is given to the body. It is important to have information concerning the client's religion and culture, so that appropriate attention may be given to the body. Usually the body will be washed and the limbs straightened; the nails will be cleaned and the hair arranged. A shroud will be put on and the body covered with a clean sheet.

Statutory responsibilities

The statutory responsibilities following a death are as follows:

- A death certificate is issued by the doctor present at the death or called immediately following a death. This is given to the relatives of the deceased.
- If there are any unusual circumstances, the death may have to be reported to a coroner.
- The death certificate is taken to the Registrar of Births, Deaths and Marriages.
- Funeral or cremation arrangements are made after the death has been registered.

Helping and supporting the bereaved

When someone dies, the people who have been close to the person during his or her life will be affected by the death in a variety of ways. It is helpful if carers can understand something about the grieving process.

After someone dies, those who remain usually pass through a period of grief. The timing of this is not precise, but there are four distinct stages which can be identified:

- Stage 1 – numbness, denial and shock.
- Stage 2 – yearning and protest including sighing, sobbing and guilt.
- Stage 3 – despair and disorganisation, including a feeling of hopelessness which can go on for two years or more.
- Stage 4 – reorganisation of life, recognising that the death has occurred.

Carers can help during this period by assisting with the actual tasks concerned with mourning. The bereaved person needs to accept the reality of the loss and then to feel the pain of grief. After this, adjustment to life without the deceased is possible.

Carers can be supportive during this process by giving time to listen, showing patience and understanding.

ACTIVITY

Have you experienced the death of someone close to you? If you feel you are able, discuss your feelings and actions after the death.

Make notes of the things that helped and comforted you.

▲ *Helping and supporting the bereaved*   © *Sam Tanner, courtesy of Age Concern England*

ASSIGNMENT 1

Designing a room

You are a care assistant in a home for elderly people. An 86-year-old woman has been offered a room in the establishment. She has limited mobility and she has asked you to help her make recommendations to the establishment's Head about decorations and furnishings for her room.

Tasks

1 Make a drawing of the room, including situation and dimensions of windows, doors, and sanitary appliances.

2 Choose paint and wallpaper, and work out the costs.

3 Select curtains and carpet, and work out the costs.

4 Select furniture (bed, chairs, tables, etc.) and cost them.

5 Include sample materials and colour charts, etc. with your choices.

6 Write a full explanation to justify your recommendations.

Behavioural and community studies – the family

AIMS

► To define *the family*.

► To examine what the family does and its role.

► To discuss how the family has changed.

► To consider child abuse and poverty.

► To discover what help is available.

INTRODUCTION

This chapter begins with an analysis of *the family* today and the effects upon its members of the changing roles of men and women, both in the family itself and in society generally. We will look at different family structures and explore the contradictory nature of the family, for example the part the family plays in child abuse. Chapter 3 deals with wider issues in society which affect our behaviour, such as housing, social class, groups and racism.

THE FAMILY

Most people understand that the word 'family' refers to a group of people who may be related to each other by blood and/or marriage. Everyone knows what a family is – mum, dad, brothers, sisters, grandparents. Look around at your own family and compare it with those of your friends. It is clear that some families are large, some small, some have both parents and others only one.

We are going to examine three aspects of the family:

- What is the family?
- What does the family do?
- Has the family changed?

What is the family?

Media images (images on TV, in magazines and newspapers) of family life would have us believe that families live in beautifully decorated homes. Mothers are always glamorous, patient and perfectly groomed. Similarly, fathers are well-built, smart and friendly. Such parents appear in their new car with their 'designer' children. The reality may be something quite different.

You may find that many of you have written down similar points from the above activity. Marriage or a partnership may have featured in some of your definitions, but of course there are many single-parent families. However, the majority of people in Britain are married and living in a family unit, with or without children.

There are many ways in which the family can be organised and still carry out its basic tasks. In some societies, the family structure is very different from that which we know in Europe. For example, in Britain it is customary for one wife to have one husband; this is termed *monogamy*. In Tibet, however, one woman may have several husbands, *polyandry*. In some countries, (mainly Islamic societies) one husband may have several wives, *polygamy*.

In Israel there is a very different type of support network, called the *kibbutz*. Here, children live in special children's houses looked after by a mother substitute and only spend a limited time with their parents. Men and women, freed from childcare responsibilities, work on farms and in factories. The planners of the kibbutz approach were trying to create a new society, but the experiment has been less successful than hoped.

Family size

There is no doubt that the family is now smaller than it used to be. In Victorian times the average family would have about six children. The average number of children in families containing dependent children has remained the same since 1981, after falling from 2.0 children to 1.8 children per family between 1971 and 1981. The average today is just over two.

What does the family do?

Socialisation and education

A society needs its new members to be socialised into its patterns of behaviour, values and rules. *Socialisation* means to make social, to become part of society. Professionals could do this, but throughout history the family has had this responsibility. In British society, parents and carers pass these values and rules onto children. Gradually and unconsciously children are informed of the norms of the society that they live in. This process is never-ending, it continues throughout life, but the part that the family plays in socialisation is very important. The bonds between parents and children allow a natural method of transmitting the values and norms of society.

ACTIVITY

Consider and list the skills that a child may **not** develop between birth and five years if they are denied all social contact. You could do this in pairs or small groups.

Parents also 'educate' their children. Early stimulation and the availability of opportunities for development can make a great difference to a child's overall performance, both academically and with regard to life skills. Children also learn how to behave and interact with other children and adults in a nursery, playgroup or school.

Reproduction

A successful society must be able to replace those who have died, otherwise it will become extinct. The family in our society regulates the production of children and, as long as everyone sticks to the rules, provides the child with a home, love and food. The family structure is one means of bringing children into the world and so maintaining the population. It also provides the mother and father with a stable emotional and sexual relationship. The family seems to be a natural grouping, able to meet many of the basic needs of society.

Security

Some writers have stressed the importance of the family in terms of providing emotional satisfaction and security for its members. The family and home is a place where people can relax and be themselves, and test out relationships with confidence. Others argue that the family is a limiting factor in building relationships in that it stifles personal development, causing strain, tension and discontent.

The family may not only provide emotional and psychological support but practical care also. Some writers argue that this caring function has, in Britain at least, been taken over by the National Health Service. However, many people needing care are still looked after in their own homes by relatives, either living in the household or nearby.

Has the family changed?

Before the Industrial Revolution (1740–1850) and the factory system, many families worked as a unit of production. Parents and children worked together to produce goods, such as textiles or farm produce. The home was often the work-place and the aim of meeting family needs would be incorporated with the need to work and produce. Women often played a major role in the production of goods as well as looking after the children. Families were usually comprised of parents and children only, called *nuclear families*. Few families had surviving grandparents as many people died in their early forties. It has been estimated that before 1820 only about one in ten families had grandparents.

With the development of the factory as a workplace and the introduction of compulsory education (by 1880 education was compuslory for 5 to 13-year-olds, although difficult to enforce) family roles and responsibilities changed. By the beginning of this century most people were earning wages outside the home. Family size increased and people began to live longer. The result was that many grandparents lived longer. This *extended* family of children, parents and grandparents, living in the same household or nearby, survived into the middle of this century in many communities and in some may still survive today. It is important to remember that the extended family is not the same thing as a big family. The extended family is made up of a series of nuclear families linked by blood, marriage or adoption.

▲ *An extended family*

Today the *nuclear* family is the norm. This family consists of couples and their children living alone. Relatives in many cases may be living long distances from the nuclear family. As people become more mobile they tend to move large distances, mainly for employment, and thus move away from parents and grandparents.

There are advantages and disadvantages of both kinds of family, *extended* and *nuclear*. In small groups, discuss these and summarise your conclusions. You could present your conclusions to the rest of the group in a short presentation.

The changing role of men and women

The role of women in the family has changed the most over the years. Many women have worked outside the home to support the family since pre-industrial times. In 1825, about one-quarter of women worked outside the home; today over half do. Much of this increase has been due to the recent trend for mothers to return to work more quickly after childbirth.

Women work today for a number of reasons. A woman's income may be essential for the survival of the family or alternatively a woman's decision to work may be based on the desire to raise the standard of living of the family. Social reasons may also play a part. Mothers may feel isolated at home with young children and enjoy the company of others which the work place provides. Work may also provide status and financial security for a woman. Despite the recession of the late 1980s, the proportion of working mothers with dependent children has increased to about 60 per cent from 49 per cent in 1981. Most of these mothers (approximately two-thirds), work part-time.

The rise of women's liberation and of modern feminism has raised questions about the role of women, and an inevitable consequence of this process has been the growing questioning of what a man's role involves. Male roles within the family are also changing. Men tend to be more involved in childcare and domestic tasks than ever before. The traditional, authoritative figure of the dominant husband or father whose word went unchallenged is associated with images of the

▲ *The changing role of men*
Reproduced courtesy of Sally and Richard Greenhill

past. Some people argue that the father is no longer essential to the economic survival of the family. Some men are very active as family members, others take a more passive role. What happens in your family?

ACTIVITY

Who does what in your house?
Look at the list below and write down who generally carries out each task. Discuss your findings within groups in your class.

- Decorating
- Mending a plug
- Cooking
- Washing
- Buying birthday presents
- Arranging social outings for the family
- Ironing
- Cleaning windows
- Shopping
- Cleaning the car
- Clearing away after meals
- Washing up
- Giving out pocket money.

What are the differences between men and women?

There are two sorts of differences between men and women – sex differences and gender differences. Sociologists make a distinction between *sex* and *gender*. The term *sex* stands for biological differences while the term *gender* stands for the social and cultural differences between men and women. For example, sexual differences may refer to differences in the ability to bear children, whereas social differences (gender) refer to differences in dress, occupation, leisure activities, personality differences and differences in emotional approach or assumed masculine characteristics, such as aggression.

Traditionally, it has been stated that women are soft, illogical, timid, passive, emotional and dependent. On the other hand, men are hard, logical, brave, aggressive and independent. In the past, these roles have been allocated to each of the two sexes and, as a result, men have been expected to fill certain positions in life and women others. These roles are called *stereotypes*.

Consider a party scenario. Men and women will be standing together in pairs or small groups. The men may be found closer to the source of the drink. They may be drinking pints of beer. They will be wearing clothes that approximate to their working clothes, for example, trousers or jeans and a jacket or sweater. On the other hand, the women at the party will be dressed more decoratively and colourfully. They will not be in their everyday clothes but in special party clothes supplemented by make-up and jewellery. They will be more likely to drink wine or spirits. What do these differences imply?

Gender differentiation

These examples given above demonstrate the wide-ranging and deep-rooted character of *gender differentiation* in our society. For example, it is often assumed that women have the primary responsibility for caring in our society. Look around at the number of boys, if any, in your class. This assumption derives from the notion that a woman's place is in the home, looking after family members. This role extends to caring for the elderly, the infirm and the sick. These notions also apply to the jobs women are expected to do. Women are in the majority when it comes to being nurses, nursery nurses, teachers or social workers, but there are few women engineers, surgeons or plumbers.

What explanation can we give for these differences between men and women? One response is to say it is 'natural'; the biological differences determine the way men and women behave.

We have seen, when looking at the family, that although women must bear children they need not look after them. In times of war in Britain, the state looked after children to allow women to work in the factories, only to shift back again to the 'normal' situation when the war ended. Biologists increasingly seem to agree that each one of us has a particular mix of sexual characteristics. We cannot be male and female at the same time, but we all have different mixes of the male and female characteristics within us.

Stereotyping in the family

What part does the family play in *stereotyping*? We have seen what a large and very important part the family plays in our lives, particularly in our early years. This socialisation gives us our first lessons in stereotyping by following what our parents do, the way we are dressed, the games and toys we use and the roles we are told are appropriate in different social situations.

During your next placement at a nursery or school observe how boys and girls behave while they are playing.

What games do girls play? Are they different in any way from those played by boys?

▲ *Children playing at the Patmore Centre*   © *Jenny Matthews, courtesy of Save the Children Fund*

At a more general level, a number of social changes have taken place in the role of men, such as loss of the traditional, male, 'bread-winner' role. Paid work has been and remains important for most men as it defines masculinity. It is for this reason that changing patterns of employment, and particularly increasing unemployment, may threaten 'masculinity'. In Britain, thousands of men have suddenly found themselves incapable of fulfilling the requirements of the male gender role. Unemployment may mean loss of status, increasing frustration, domestic difficulties and in some cases even a reassertion of a certain sort of 'masculinity' through violence.

ACTIVITY

Arrange to interview an elderly person. This can be someone you know. Try to find out what family life was like when he or she was young.

Ask questions such as:

- What was the size of the family?
- Who lived in the household?
- Did any of the family move from the area?
- Have the roles of husband and wife changed over the years?
- What jobs did men do and how did they find them?

ONE-PARENT FAMILIES

During the 1970s, there was an increase in the number of families headed by lone parents. In 1990, 18 per cent of all families with dependent children were headed by lone parents compared with 8 per cent in 1971. Today, almost one in five families is now headed by a lone parent, making up 20 per cent of total households. Rising numbers of unmarried, divorced and separated parents have increased the number of people bringing up children on their own to more than 1.25 million. A *one-parent family* (or *single-parent family*) is usually defined as:

'a mother or father living without a spouse (and not cohabiting) with his or her never-married dependent child or children'.

One-parent families tend to have a lower income on average than two-parent families. Two out of every three single parents depend on Social Security and other income-related benefits. The fast-growing number of lone mothers, combined with the rising number of people living alone, means that only one in four households consists of married or cohabiting couples with dependent children.

What do you think are the possible advantages or disadvantages of being a single parent family for both parent and children?

THE FAMILY'S ROLE IN CARING FOR THE SICK AND ELDERLY

An estimated 6 million adults are caring for less-capable friends and relatives at home. Around 25 per cent spend more than 20 hours per week caring for a dependent relative; approximately 60 per cent spend 60 hours a week doing so. Women are more likely to be carers than men, but the difference is not very marked. There are about 3.5 million women compared to 2.5 million men, so this large number of male carers cannot be discounted.

Who are these millions of carers? Carers are ordinary, untrained people doing an exacting job and like other ordinary people they have needs and feelings. Carers may feel lonely and isolated as they may not be able to leave the house very often or for very long.

ACTIVITY

1 Write down what you think the feelings of a carer with a very dependent relative might be.

2 Did your list include any of the following?
   - Embarrassed at the condition or habits of their dependant.
   - Embarrassment at having to do personal tasks for close relatives.
   - Anger at lack of help from the statutory services.
   - A sense of loss that the person they are caring for may seem a stranger to them.
   - Feelings of guilt at the possibility that they themselves might need help or counselling.

Carers often have a sense of individual, rather than shared and collective, responsibility. Many carers suffer such physical and emotional stress that their own health suffers. When they become ill, the person they are caring for is often left without support. The mental and physical strain of caring for a very dependent person can occasionally lead to the carer abusing the person they are looking after.

Although there have always been people who have cared for their sick and dependent friends and relatives, there is now public recognition of their situation in society and governments have stressed the importance of the carer's role. Recent government publications (*Caring for People: Community Care in the Next Decade and Beyond 1990*) has support for carers as one of its key objectives.

THE FAMILY AND CHILD ABUSE

Children are vulnerable members of society. They are physically incapable of protecting themselves from adults. In the last century, the developing industrial society subjected young children to great cruelty and abuse in the factories and workshops of Victorian England. At home, discipline was usually rigid with its 'spare the rod and spoil the child' attitude.

In 1899, as a result of general concern about the ill-treatment of children, a bill was passed in Parliament. This was called the 'Children's Charter' and allowed for the formation of the National Society for the Prevention of Cruelty to Children (NSPCC).

The actual term *child abuse* was first used in 1946 when a paediatric radiologist drew attention to the 'unexplained' fractures of the long bones of young children. By 1955, many of these injuries were thought to have been inflicted by parents. The emotive phrase 'Battered child syndrome' was introduced in 1961 and since then many reports have appeared which show that this problem affects a wide spectrum of religious, social and economic societies.

The deliberate choice by Dr Kempe, a US paediatrician, of the term 'The battered child' (in 1961) to describe injuries to children caused by parents has done much to produce an awareness of this problem and it has attracted considerable attention in the press and elsewhere. At present, we know little of the true extent of *child abuse*; there is no clear or accepted national or international definition of this term.

Children may suffer from different types of abuse. There is *physical abuse* when a child is physically injured and *psychological abuse* when a child may be treated and spoken to in a hurtful manner, or neglected or deprived of the emotional factors necessary for a stable life. A child may also be sexually abused when his or her body may be used to gratify an adult's sexual desire.

Reasons for abuse

The reasons why children are abused are varied and it is impossible to say precisely what makes an adult abuse a child. Sometimes there is a pattern of abuse in the family, so that the victims of abuse actually become abusers later on in life. Some people suggest that parents who batter may be re-creating their own child-hood circumstances when rearing their own children.

Parents who abuse their children share a number of characteristics. The parent may be socially isolated and fails to establish a satisfactory marital relationship. A high proportion of abusing mothers may be unmarried, divorced or separated and they tend to have a high level of physical and psychiatric problems. Fathers may be unemployed or have criminal records while abuse is occurring. Children are abused by their mothers, but fathers may also abuse their children.

The abused child

Abuse can occur against any child of any age, but it is more frequently reported in children under the age of three years; the highest proportion occurring in children under six months. Boys tend to be abused more than girls. Sometimes several children in a family are abused; sometimes only one is singled out.

Professionals and the abused child

All professionals working within or related to the field of child abuse, such as social workers, teachers, nursery nurses, doctors and nurses have to face the great responsibility that suspected abuse brings. This fear means extra stress for such staff. However, Social Services staff have the main responsibility for the protection of children. They have a *statutory duty* (a duty by law) to investigate any complaint and to provide support and care to families and children.

ACTIVITY

Working in small groups find out:

1 Where the NSPCC is located in your area.

2 What work it does for families and children.

FAMILIES AND POVERTY

Individuals and families receive their income from a variety of sources. Many people rely on the state for their income in the form of Social Security or other forms of benefit. About one in five people live below the official poverty line. The *poverty line*, as defined by the EEC, is half the average wage (£268 a week in 1990), which works out at £134 a week.

There are also great differences between the lowest and highest paid. For example, the results of a survey carried out in 1990 of 8 000 jobs on offer in a Job Shop, revealed that 3 000 paid £2.50 per hour and about 1 000 paid £3.50 per hour. Those people on £2.50 per hour and doing a 40-hour week would earn £100 per week, well below the average earnings in 1990 of £268 a week and £34 below the poverty line. Most of the jobs on offer were part-time and in the catering trade, or in offices and shops offering a wage below the EEC poverty line.

What is poverty and how do we define it?

There are a number of definitions of poverty. The two main ones we will consider are *absolute poverty* and *relative poverty*.

Absolute poverty

People may be in *absolute poverty* if they have insufficient on which to survive. Many people in the Third World could be described as suffering from absolute poverty. In the 1870s, Charles Booth, a social reformer, was one of the first to examine the life of the poor. He defined poverty as a situation under which it was impossible to live a healthy life. In 1899, Seebohm Rowntree, another social reformer, used the term 'absolute poverty' when he carried out his survey of poverty in the city of York.

Rowntree worked out that a family with three children needed 21 shillings and 8 pence per week to live on, at that time. This amount covered only what was absolutely necessary for survival. For example, the food considered necessary did not include any tinned food (considered a luxury) or money for birthday or Christmas presents. Rowntree's definition of the poverty line was more precise than Booth's ('the minimum provision needed to maintain health and working efficiency') and was based on food, clothing and housing. Rowntree distinguished two types of poverty: *primary* and *secondary*. Families who suffered *primary poverty* had total earnings which were insufficient to maintain physical efficiency. Those suffering from *secondary poverty* had sufficient income but used it, for example, on drink.

Relative poverty

Theoretically, no one in Britain should be in absolute poverty because of the development of the Welfare State. However, some people either refuse to accept, or are not aware of, the benefits they are entitled to, and so could be said to be in absolute poverty.

During the 1950s, after the introduction of welfare benefits, a notion developed that poverty no longer existed in Britain. This notion was challenged by a number of academics who stated that poverty did exist in a relative form.

Those in *relative poverty* are said to have 'resources so seriously below those commanded by the average individual or family that they are, in effect, excluded from ordinary living patterns, customs and activities'. This is poverty by comparison and the comparison is with our reference group, i.e. the people to whom we think we should be compared. In addition, what may be considered poverty today may not have been considered poverty 20 years ago. This is because basic expectations and standards of living have been improved.

ACTIVITY

1 Make a list of things that a family today would consider necessary in order to lead an ordinary life.

2 Compare this list with one of, say, 50 years ago. Are the same things listed?

Measuring poverty

Measuring poverty is difficult because people's expectations change. You may consider a TV or radio as necessary today, but 30 years ago would this have been the case? People are not necessarily in poverty all the time. They may be poor during the period that they have dependent children, during unemployment or when they retire.

In 1978, a government report argued that 7 per cent of those in poverty were unemployed, the elderly accounted for 33 per cent and the low-paid for 40 per cent. Those below the unofficial poverty line determined by the EEC, i.e. half the average weekly wage, have increased by nearly seven million in the past nine years to nearly ten million people. The government's own figures show that the number of people below the official poverty line, i.e. those qualifying for supplementary benefit, rose from 3.7 million in 1979 to nearly 8 million by 1987.

What causes poverty?

Many families get along quite well until they lose their income because the bread-winner has been made unemployed or becomes ill. Many workers receive low pay and many earn less than the level of supplementary benefit. It is often necessary for a husband and wife to work long hours to support a family. Since families with young children are more likely to be poor than those without children, large families are particularly vulnerable.

Other groups particularly prone to suffer from poverty are, for example, the elderly. Pensions are often inadequate and the elderly are forced to seek extra help from the state in the form of benefits. Many old people refuse to ask for such help, preferring instead to keep their independence. In 1985, one in three old age pensioners who were entitled to extra help did not claim it. Disabled people are also vulnerable because they may find it difficult to secure a job.

THE HELP AVAILABLE

Some assistance can be made available through voluntary organisations, but the main form of help for those with little or no income is through state benefits which are administered by the Department of Social Security (DSS). The main benefits are outlined below, but you should find out about them in more detail and check the current rates of benefit by reading the DSS publications which you can get from post offices, DSS offices or welfare benefit offices provided by many local authorities.

Many benefits are contributory, which means that you must have been in work and paid a certain number of National Insurance Contributions (NICs) in order to be able to claim any help. Other benefits are *means tested*. This means that other forms of income you may have (for example, family credit, rent rebates and allowances or free dental treatment) are taken into account when deciding whether you can claim the benefit or how much benefit you are entitled to.

Income Support

The Income Support scheme is a means tested benefit designed to help those who are:

- unemployed;
- retired;
- bringing up a child or children alone;
- too ill or disabled to work;
- widowed.

To claim, you must be over 16 years of age and you must not work more than 24 hours per week.

Family Credit

Family Credit is designed to support those families in low-paid work, both employed or self-employed, who are not entitled to Income Support. The family must have at least one child and one parent must work at least 24 hours per week.

People on either Income Support or Family Credit can claim extra help, such as free school meals, free prescriptions, free dental treatment and help with glasses.

Go to your local DSS office or post office and pick up booklet FC1.

1 Check out how low a family's income has to be before they can claim Family Credit.

2 What other benefits might a family claiming Family Credit be entitled to?

The Social Fund

This scheme has replaced a previous one which gave one-off payments to people in need. The Social Fund provides interest-free loans or grants. Applicants' savings are checked and loans may be refused if there has been a heavy demand on the scheme in the local area. The Social Fund can assist in the following ways:

- By making a **maternity payment** if the applicant is on Income Support or Family Credit. This grant does not have to be repaid.
- By making a **funeral payment** for those on Income Support or Family Credit. If there is any money in the estate of the deceased person, it will be used to pay back the loan.
- By making **community care grants** which are designed to support people living independently in the community. For example, a person who has a handicap may be able to get a grant for a washing machine. This grant, like the maternity payment, does not have to be repaid.
- By making **crisis loans** which are grants provided for those who have experienced a crisis, for example, a house fire or theft where all their money was lost. This grant has to be repaid.
- By making **budgeting loans** which are designed to support those who have been getting Income Support for 26 weeks. These loans can be obtained for items such as a bed or a cooker, but again must be repaid.

Before the Social Fund officers decide to approve any loan or grant, you must be in a position to pay it back. If the applicant has other debts the application may be refused, even if the need is vital. Those applications that are accepted will be given an offer in writing stating how the loan is to be repaid.

ASSIGNMENT 2

Welfare benefits

You are on duty in a local advice centre and the following people come into the centre asking for advice on benefits. You must explain to them what benefits they are entitled to claim, the leaflets they should read and how they must go about making a claim.

- Mary is married with two children. Her husband is working 20 hours a week and they have no savings.

- The Jones family gets Family Credit and have suffered a fire in the children's bedroom. An aged relative has also died.

- John is disabled. He was discharged from hospital a few months ago. His washing machine has broken down and he needs warm blankets now that winter is approaching.

- Alice is bringing up two children alone. She is earning £16 000 a year and works for 36 hours a week.

Behavioural and community studies – housing, social class and race

AIMS

▶ To understand the basic physical and emotional needs for housing and the problems of rehousing.

▶ To learn about class and group structures.

▶ To realise the impact of different forms of mass media.

▶ To understand the issues of race and the need to be sensitive to the requirements of ethnic groups.

HOUSING

Shelter from the weather and the world is a basic human need. For many people, home is not only a place of accommodation, but also a source of their physical and mental well-being. Home should be where one can relax away from the tensions and pressures of the work place. A person's house is regarded as their territory. People talk of places which feel like 'home' and when away from home may suffer from home sickness. People may be judged because of where they live, the type of house they live in, whether it is owned or rented. So housing is much more than bricks and mortar.

Developments in housing

The majority of people in this country live in homes which consist of a kitchen, a living room, two to four bedrooms, a bathroom and a toilet. This type of accommodation is a very great improvement on houses which were available in the last century when many were built to accommodate a growing population and expanding workforce. In the middle of the last century, one street alone in London had 27 houses with over 1 000 people living in them; an average of eight people per room or 40 per house. It is hard to imagine today that in the 1850s over one-third of the City of Liverpool's population lived in cellars, often below sea level, and in the damp with no natural light. Liverpool has come a long way since then, but back-to-back houses, without rear entrances or gardens, still exist in many of our large cities today.

Insanitary conditions in the 1800s were a danger to health. Only after a number of outbreaks of cholera and typhoid did the state take some action. Public health laws were passed, clean water was piped to houses, drainage was made compulsory and gradually cities became less unhealthy places. Only after the First World War did the state recognise the need to get involved in the housing market. Central government paid sums of money to local authorities for every house built and so the idea of council houses was introduced.

The problems of rehousing and high-rise flats

During the Second World War when many thousands of homes were damaged or destroyed, local authorities took the opportunity to clear away the slums and build new homes. In many instances, they replaced this poor housing stock with high-rise blocks of flats, which could be easily and cheaply erected without taking up much land. In many cases, these flats were of a higher standard than the housing they replaced, and for the first time people had good sanitation, bathrooms and hot and cold water.

However, rehousing and slum clearance also meant destroying whole neighbourhoods and the sense of community that existed in them. People who were moved often felt isolated, lonely and missed the support of the extended family.

ACTIVITY

What disadvantages can be associated with living in high-rise flats?

You might like to consider some of the following:

- problems of noise;
- lack of privacy;
- access problems;
- lack of play facilities for children;
- lack of community spirit;
- difficulties with stairs or lifts.

The problems associated with high-rise flats caused, in many occupants, mental and emotional distress. Lack of social facilities caused frustration, which in a number of areas led to violence and vandalism. Many local housing authorities later realised that this type of housing was a mistake and in recent years authorities like Sheffield, Leeds and Liverpool have demolished these flats and built conventional houses.

Despite the attempts of housing authorities, over 2 million houses were substandard in 1981. Many were unfit for habitation, in need of major repairs or lacked such basic amenities as hot water, a bathroom or a toilet.

Home ownership

In 1971, 49 per cent of households owned their own home; by 1986 over 62 per cent did so and approximately 26 per cent lived in council housing. Over the years, there has been a decline in private renting, accounting for 12 per cent of accommodation in 1971 and only 5 per cent by 1986.

It is extremely expensive to buy your own home, but the state may help people to do so in two ways. It allows some people a tax incentive by allowing tax relief on mortgages. The state will also help some owners to improve their houses by giving improvement grants.

Homelessness

Many people, for whatever reason, either cannot or do not live in a house. Many arguments have been advanced about the origins of homelessness. Is the problem caused by housing shortages or is it brought about by family breakdown? Those who believe that the shortage of houses is the cause point to the fall in local authority housing supply by over 80 per cent between 1978 and 1988. Private, rented accommodation is also falling and this affects those who cannot afford to buy their own houses.

In 1989, 148 000 households were accepted as homeless. This was double the percentage who were homeless in 1979. The commonest cause of homelessness is disputes with relatives, friends or parents. An increasing cause is default on mortgage payments. Many one-parent, homeless families and couples with children live in bed and breakfast accommodation, most existing on state benefits.

The voluntary organisation Charity, which works with the homeless, says that there are about 3 million people without their own homes in Britain.

▲ Sheltered housing   Photograph courtesy of McCarthy & Stone

Sheltered housing

Sheltered housing has its beginnings in the medieval alms houses; a concept which was developed during the 1920s and 1930s. The first comprehensive study of sheltered housing was carried out in 1981 by the Joseph Rowntree Memorial Trust. This study defined sheltered housing as having:

- a resident warden;
- an alarm system fitted to each dwelling;
- the occupancy restricted to elderly people only;
- accommodation all on one site.

There are, however, various degrees of 'shelter' based upon the amount of communal facilities provided.

Why have sheltered housing?

Sheltered housing fulfils a housing need – it meets the special needs of many elderly people. Sheltered housing also reduces the possibility of emergencies occurring, through the presence of a warden. This type of housing offers more choice to elderly people, as it is an alternative to residential care. It also helps to combat loneliness by offering the possibility of wider social contacts and it fosters independence.

SOCIAL CLASS

Have you a good set of teeth? Do you save or spend money? Do you expect to live to a ripe old age? Were you a breast-fed baby? How do you feel about nakedness? These questions may seem strange to you, but in fact research indicates that your answers may be linked to your social class position. Before we go on to discuss this, let us first look at social class. How do you know which one you belong to?

Social class is a form of social stratification, a system for putting people into strata or layers. In Britain, the Registrar-General, a government official, collects data on all births, deaths and marriages, and census data every ten years. Since the beginning of this century, the Registrar-General has grouped people into five social classes, from a list of 20 000 jobs, as a way of classifying people. The groupings are based on the income, status, skill and educational level of each job.

Classes 1–3 are usually what we would call the middle class and Classes 4–5 may be referred to as the working class. Examples of jobs belonging to the various classes are shown in Table 3.1.

Middle class	Class 1	Professional	Doctors, dentists, solicitors
	Class 2	Managerial	Managers, teachers, nurses
	Class 3	Non-manual	Clerks, typists, travel agents
		Skilled manual	Electricians, hairdressers, cooks
Working class	Class 4	Semi-skilled manual	Postmen or women, farm workers
	Class 5	Unskilled manual	Cleaners, labourers

Table 3.1 *The five social classes*

Why do we consider education and training as more important than the money a person earns? A nurse may earn less than a cook or labourer, but the nurse is in Class 2, the cook in Class 3 and labourer in Class 5. Why do you think this is so? Does the nurse contribute more to society than the cook?

The classification is an objective way of looking at social class; it is decided on the basis of your job. It is important to realise that if a person is allocated to a certain class bracket it does not mean that they will behave in a particular way. One other way to define social class is to ask people to what social class they feel that they belong. What social class do you belong to?

Movement between the classes

How do people move between these social classes? One way is to marry out of, or into, a class. A doctor's daughter who marries a postman moves out of Class 1 into Class 4. A cleaner's daughter who qualifies as a solicitor moves into Class 1. But a man who marries a woman in a different social class does not move. Why do you think this is?

Why might a person rise up the social scale?

Discuss the following points in relation to a person's ability to move up the social class scale:

- education;
- knowing the 'right people', i.e. 'contacts';
- working hard;
- intelligence;
- 'making a good match';
- being ambitious.

It is important to respond to people as individuals and not fall into the trap of stereotyping. It is easy to generalise and make assumptions about people; for example, it would be wrong to state that all people in Class 5 have unhealthy diets and that people in Class 2 have good eating habits. There are many issues that can be discussed in social class terms, like leisure patterns or voting behaviour, but perhaps the clearest issue to understand is the relationship between health and social class.

Health and social class

A 1980 government report *Inequalities In Health* concluded that despite the existence of a health service there remained a marked class gradient in standards of health, with substantial increases in the rates of both mortality and morbidity (illness) as one moves down the social scale.

1 Discuss and list the possible explanations for the conclusions above.

2 Compare your list with your class colleagues.

GROUPS

We all seem to have a need to belong to one form of group or other. You have already looked at one important group, the family. This group is usually the first that you experience. It is the first group where you will learn that other people have rights and that they and you must conform to rules and regulations. You learn how to behave with other people, how to eat and play games. Later on, children meet other family groups and form groups at school. At school you will also have experienced groups operating – groups of particular friends, sports groups or groups of bullies – all of which helped to train you for the adult world.

1 List five groups that you now belong to and the reasons why you chose them.

2 When you have done this, explain to others in your class why the groups you chose to highlight are important to you.

Here is a list of groups, some of which you may have listed as belonging to:

- church
- family
- sports club
- football team
- political party
- ethnic group
- voluntary organisation
- student group.

Why do people form groups?

For security

People form groups for security as they are naturally sociable and want to be with others, sharing common ideas, values and pleasures. As a member of a group, people enjoy the companionship of others with the same interests, ideas and attitudes. They feel safe and confident as one of a group sharing similar aims and objectives.

To share or help

People may join a group to help others out of some commitment. This could be a voluntary group or charity. Alternatively, they may want to share an experience with others in a group, such as the desire to play football well in a team. These needs are different from joining a club simply to enjoy the company of others.

To get things done

Personal objectives may be more easily attained in a group. Individuals can often achieve aims as part of a group that they would not otherwise manage alone. One person may not be able to stop a development in a nature reserve, but as a member of a pressure group this aim may be achieved.

1 Choose one group to which you belong. Write down what you believe to be:
   a) The aims of the group.
   b) How the group works.
   c) What your contribution is to the group.
   d) What the group demands of you.

2 What kind of group is it?

Primary groups

Primary groups are usually small enough to allow the members to form close personal relationships. As a result the whole group develops a strong sense of solidarity and individuals rely on each other. The family is one important primary group, but others include sports teams, street gangs and small groups of people, such as a few black families in a street containing a majority of white families, or disabled students in a class with a majority of able-bodied students.

Secondary groups

Secondary groups are large bodies in which the members have looser ties than in primary groups. Many secondary groups are joined on a voluntary basis, such as football supporters' clubs and trade unions, but many others have involuntary membership, such as racial groups, schools or social class. Both primary and secondary groups have unity and share many of the same rules and pressures.

ACTIVITY

- What regulations and rules apply to the groups that you belong to?
- How did you get to know of the group?
- Do you have to wear a uniform, badge or special clothes, or speak a special language?
- Do you have to carry out certain rituals or admission procedures?

Make notes on the above and keep them in your file.

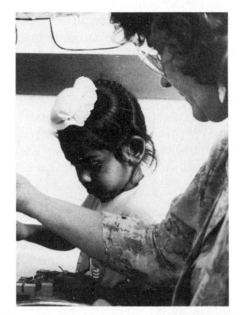

▲ *Membership of a group can be shown by dress,
as in the case of this young Sikh boy*
© *Prodeepta Das, courtesy of Save the Children Fund*

How do groups work?

People who belong to a group usually have a strong bond which makes them feel very differently about people not in their group, the 'out group'. Members of a group may discriminate against those who are not in their group. Think of your class group. Are there any members who are always picked on or blamed for anything that goes wrong?

ACTIVITY

How would you deal with a class colleague who constantly interrupts the class.

Discuss with your classmates how you might deal with this problem.

Group pressure

Pressure on group members to conform to the group rules is very strong, resulting in people doing things that they would not normally do. If the group drinks, individuals who do not normally do so may drink. Normally placid individuals may become very violent and aggressive in a group. Some members fear the consequences if they do not follow the will of the group. Think how you would feel if all your classmates decided not to involve you in their activities. Belonging to a group can lift from you the responsibility for making decisions. It is much easier, in many cases, to follow group thinking or activities than to take your own stance on an issue.

ACTIVITY

Form a group of five or six in the class. Pretend that you have belonged to this group for a long time.

Your friends in the group want you to smoke a cigarette, something you have never done before. How would you go about resisting this pressure?

Why belong to a group?

Membership of a group can result in the following benefits:

- pleasure and satisfaction from sharing a common interest;
- security which can engender confidence;
- learning opportunities – individuals can learn skills in the group which can be practised in personal life;
- opportunities to develop leadership skills;
- experience of democratic processes.

ACTIVITY

The aim of this activity is to enable half your class colleagues to observe the other half in achieving some group tasks. The whole activity may take about two hours.

Read through the whole activity before you begin.

Task 1

As a group, decide how to assess an assignment that you have just been given.

You may wish to consider some of the following assessment strategies:

- percentage marks;
- pass or fail (no marks given);
- fail, pass, merit, distinction (no marks given).

Task 2

As a group, decide who should assess the assignment and why.

Assessors may be:

- college staff;
- college staff and students;
- students as a group;
- other students on the course; or
- another option.

Recording interaction within the group

Procedure
One group performs the tasks and the other observes them. The performing group sits in a circle. The other group members place themselves where they can see the interaction between the members of the first group.

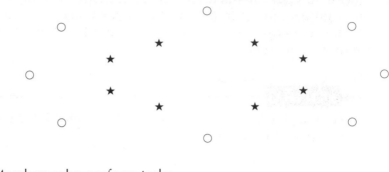

★: Members who perform tasks
○: Members who observe.

What to observe
- Who speaks to whom?
- How often do they speak?

Recording interactions
Use a diagram like the one illustrated below to record the interaction between group members.

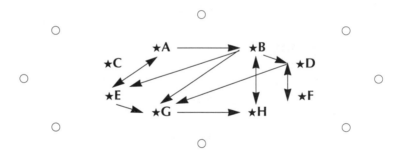

X: Member of group performing tasks
→: Direction of communication

Member **B** is leader of this group; member **C** seems to be left out.

Another method you can use is to make a list to record:

- Who communicates non-verbally?
- Who started the discussion?
- Who speaks a lot?
- Who said very little?

Said little	Started discussion	Speaks a lot
A	D	B
F		

How can you record non-verbal communication in a group?

Folded arms	Sat back in chair	Waved hands for emphasis
B	A	D

Procedure to measure contributions

The simplest measure of behaviour in a group is how much each member says. One way to record this is to record a mark for each time a member makes a statement. The results will indicate who speaks a great deal or is silent most of the time. This procedure will *not* tell you how valuable any contribution may have been.

Contributions are usually recorded in a *tally chart* such as the one shown in Table 3.2.

A	B	C	D	G
JHT JHT	JHT JHT	JHT JHT	JHT JHT	JHT III
JHT JHT	JHT JHT		I	
	II			

Table 3.2 *Recording contributions in a tally chart*

COMMUNICATION

We have been studying communication with groups. What other types of communication do we experience? Watch two of your colleagues having a conversation in class. They take it in turn to speak or send a message and listen or receive a message. A conversation is a form of communication between people. This type of communication can be described as *interpersonal communication*.

Communication barriers

Although everyone communicates, it is true to say that good communicators are made. Most of us will have learnt communication skills from the people that we lived with, went to school with and now work with. Any communication involves a message and a medium to carry that message. We encounter difficulties in communicating with colleagues and clients. What are the communication barriers that exist, particularly between ourselves and our clients?

A number of factors can cause a social and cultural gap between ourselves and others. We may:

- be from a different ethnic background;
- be from a different social class;
- have different cultural or religious beliefs;
- have different social values; or
- even be of the opposite sex.

A client may not want to, or may be unable to, communicate with you for many reasons. They may be suffering from confusion, a handicap, illness, tiredness, pain or emotional distress.

1 Using one of the recording methods described above observe the following clients in a group situation:

- Observe a group of children in a nursery or play group. Which children talk the most or are liked by most members of the group? Is any child not talked to or played with?
- Observe a group of old people in a day room. Who talks to whom? Where do they sit?

2 Record your findings and discuss them with your class.

Mass communication

The method by which people communicate a message is known as a *medium* (the plural is *media*). When messages are sent to large members of people using technology, such as the television, newspapers or radio, we describe this as *mass media*. Mass communication is all around us. We hear the radio, watch television, read magazines or see posters. The organisation of mass communication can be vast. The finished product may be a newspaper or a television programme.

What are the main aspects of 'the media'?

Daily listeners who average 1.15 listening hours per day	Radio	
Daily readers, about 45–50 million per day	Newspapers	
Circulation of readers in the millions for popular magazines	Magazines	= **The media**
Daily audiences of approx. 1 million	Cinema	
Millions of daily viewers watching an average of over 4 hours per day	Television	

The media is an umbrella term which includes many means of communication to large numbers of people. In Britain, for example, the population is about 55 million. This communication is usually one way, from the media to the public, and is a major source of information and ideas. Each person has contact with several aspects of the media each day. The average person in Britain spends just under one-third of his or her waking time with some aspect of the media. These contacts can shape people's attitudes and can change their behaviour. This is why the media is so powerful and can and has been used for good or evil purposes.

What are the main aims of the media?

The main aims of the media are to **inform**, to **educate** or to **entertain**. How is this done?

Advertising

Over £200 million is spent each year on advertising in Britain. About 2 per cent of the price of everything we buy goes towards the cost of advertising. Advertising is used to sell us something or persuade us that something is good for us. It is almost impossible to escape from it. The advantages and disadvantages of advertising are shown in Table 3.3.

Advantages	Disadvantages
Encourages competition so helps to keep prices down	Expensive cost of advertising is added to the price of goods or services
Encourages manufacturers to improve goods to beat rivals	Tempts us to buy more than we need
Increases demands for goods which in turn creates work	Tempts us to spend more
Highlights the availability of goods and allows price comparisons	May give false claims for goods
	May stereotype people, e.g. portraying women as homemakers or men as powerful

Table 3.3 *The advantages and disadvantages of advertising*

ACTIVITY

Look at two or three newspaper and television advertisements for the past week. Look at the way women and men are portrayed in these advertisements.

1 Are women portrayed in the same way as men? In what ways are the two sexes portrayed?

2 What are the advertisements with men as the main characters trying to sell or what is their message compared to advertisements which have women as the main characters?

Newspapers

Newspapers can have a powerful effect on public attitudes and can strongly influence them. *Selectivity* is one of the methods a newspaper uses to influence people. Newspaper editors select news from a vast array of issues. News items do not select themselves. Some important items may be left out because there is not room for them or they do not suit the newspaper's ideas or politics.

Some popular papers have very large headlines but few words. Look at the *Sun* or *Daily Mirror* front pages – there is very little space for words. These newspapers exert their influence by setting things out in a sensational manner. All newspaper editors *edit* the news, i.e. they present the news item in the manner that suits their newspaper. The editor may highlight only the parts of the item that supports his or her point of view or presents someone in a good or bad light. Most newspapers are biased towards a political viewpoint and they can bend the truth to fit their perception of a situation. A newspaper, such as the *Daily Telegraph* would tend to present information from a right-wing point of view whereas the *Daily Mirror* might present a left-wing viewpoint.

▲ *The popular press*
Photograph courtesy of Express Newspapers

ACTIVITY

Which newspapers could the following headlines come from? Which is from the 'quality' press and which from the 'popular' press?

BABY BASHING DAD GETS SIX YEARS!

Father found guilty of child abuse is sentenced to six years

Newspaper readership

The readership of newspapers is very much related to social class and education. Papers are usually divided into two groups; the 'quality' newspapers and the 'popular' press. The 'quality' newspapers tend to give more cover to issues such as politics, labour relations, finance and economics, while the 'popular' press tends to give more coverage to home news, crime and sport, and includes more photographs to illustrate the news. Most of the people who left school before the age of 15 read the *Daily Mirror* or the *Sun*. Readers of the *Sun* tend to be under 30 years of age whereas readers of the *Daily Telegraph* are generally much older.

Paper	Upper-middle and middle class	Lower middle class	Skilled working class	Lower working class
Daily Mirror	5	18	42	36
Guardian	42	34	15	8
The Times	51	27	13	9
Sun	5	17	44	37

Table 3.4 Readership of some newspapers – percentage by social class
Source: *New Society*, 15 February 1979

Communication is possible without using words at all. Newspapers can influence readers by vivid photographs, cartoons and other illustrations.

ACTIVITY

1 Cut out and stick on a blank sheet of paper a photograph from a newspaper which you think is giving an effective message without the use of accompanying words.

2 What do you think is the message of the photograph you have chosen?

RACE

In recent years, race has begun to be seen as a policy issue in many caring organisations. For individual care staff and for people in multiracial communities hoping for more systematic consideration of their needs and responses, this is a significant and welcome change. It has provided the opportunity for race issues to be discussed openly and for the development of new policies and procedures.

Before we proceed with this discussion we need to examine a few definitions and look at words you may meet:

- **Minority group**. A group formed of people whose interests, religion, colour or any other common aspect is unusual or forms only a small part of the total population.
- **Multiracial**. Used to describe a society composed of different racial groups living together.
- **Racial prejudice**. A belief that one group of people, usually identified by their physical appearance, is naturally superior to other groups.
- **Ethnic**. Concerning races or nations.
- **Ethnocentric**. A belief that your group or society is at the centre of things: a failure to take into consideration other people's views.
- **Racialism or racism**. A belief in the superiority of a particular race and the treatment which discriminates against particular groups based on this belief.
- **Institutional racism**. The policies of institutions that work to continue racial ideology without acknowledging that fact. This is camouflaged racism, meaning that it is not open and visible but is hidden in the routine practices and procedures of organisations, or in statements like, 'We treat everyone equally' or 'All the clients get the same choice of meals'.

Discuss the above definitions with your tutor and others in your class. Make sure you understand them.

Why do carers need to take account of racial differences? We need to consider race as an aspect of caring for a number of reasons, such as social justice and common humanity. This cannot be done if differences are ignored or if not enough notice is taken of the circumstances and conditions of the lives of people from racial minorities in Britain.

It has been suggested that racism is a part of the British consciousness. However, the role of carers is to care for individuals whatever their race, colour or religion. Groups such as Afro-Caribbeans, Asians, Irish and Chinese are increasingly unwilling to accept the role of passive recipients of social services which others consider it appropriate to offer. Decisions may have to be made about how many special needs can be met, but social justice requires that special needs are given adequate consideration and such decisions be made fairly.

The law regarding race

All employers and providers of services are bound by the 1976 Race Relations Act. Local authorities have a duty under the Act (Section 71) to make 'appropriate arrangements' in order to 'promote equality of opportunity, and good relations, between persons of different racial groups'.

The responsibility to promote equality applies to the country as a whole – it is not confined to staff who are working in areas where there are substantial minority populations. When there are very few black people in a locality, for example, their needs may be particularly acute. Staff at all levels have to be prepared to treat with dignity and competence the few black people for whom support and care have to be arranged.

Understanding the backgrounds of minority clients

The social care worker wishing to understand and work with minority clients is presented with aspects of human experience beyond the usual range: a shared group history of migration; a struggle to sustain existence and identity in the face of hostility or indifference; different family forms and cultural backgrounds; and perceptions formed from different experiences.

An example

Relationships within Asian families are influenced by the existence of what are known as *marriage classes*. Individuals expect to find a spouse in the group within which their family intermarries. The composition of this group is determined by religious and ethnic identification, descent and economic status. Asian communities vary widely regarding the extent to which their cultural preferences stress marriage within or outside close kin. For example:

- The **Muslim** system stresses a preference for marriage within a group of closely related people. The preference is for joint households to be established between closely related males and their wives and children, to which unmarried adult males will be attached.

- **Hindu** families share a preference for marriage with the local sub-caste. Although patterns of marriage preference vary considerably between different Hindu communities, overall they tend to conform to the following caste (social class) and status distinctions:
  the *Brahmans* or priests are the highest caste;
  the *Kshatriyas* or rulers are below them;
  the *Vaishyas*, or cultivators and merchants, follow;
  the *Sudras* or servants are the lowest caste; and
  the *Untouchables* have no caste status.

The religious structure obliges the Hindu frequently to purify himself from polluting influences by ritual observances.

- **Sikhism** is an egalitarian religion. The communal meals at Sikh temples intentionally go against Hindu caste regulations. A Sikh prefers to marry out of the clans of both his or her father and mother. Usually women cannot inherit property. Nevertheless, Sikh women are influential and are accorded a full part in religious organisations and observance. Respect for hair is crucial to Sikhs and it should but uncut, clean, tidy and dressed in traditional style.

What is racial discrimination?

The law defines two kinds of racial discrimination, direct and indirect. *Direct discrimination* occurs if a person is treated less favourably than another in similar, or the same, circumstances by reason of their race. *Indirect discrimination* may occur if a racial group is treated as equal in a formal sense, but the effect may be discriminatory. For example, if a company advertised for workers and specified that applicants should live within a certain distance from the work place then the advertisement could be seen as being discriminatory if it is known that most people from ethnic groups live outside the specified geographical area. Another example of indirect discrimination arises when a headteacher refuses to relax the rules relating to school uniform and grooming. Consequently, a Sikh boy wishing to wear a turban is prevented from attending that school.

ACTIVITY

What would your response be to the following situation?

You are working on the street with a group of unemployed teenagers, all of them white but living in a run-down, inner-city area with quite large black communities. One or two of the more forceful members of the group have strong views about black people which they express in offensive racist language. Most of the other members of the group do not make such comments or show approval when they are made by the dominant members of the group.

Would you say anything about the situation, and if so what?
What else might you do?

Write down your responses and discuss them with your colleagues and tutor.

What is an ethnic group?

The House of Lords has recently laid down a check-list to help decide this question. Using this list you can establish whether or not an individual belongs to an ethnic group. The essential factors for a group are:

- a long, shared history which sets the members of the group apart from other groups;
- a cultural tradition of its own.

Some of the following may also be elements defining an ethnic group:

- a common geographic region;
- a common language;
- a common literature;
- a common religion;
- belonging to either a minority or a majority within a community.

ACTIVITY

Discuss whether you think any of the following groups of people form an ethnic group.

- People born in Scotland
- People born in Ireland
- Travellers
- English-born children of immigrants
- People born in Yorkshire.

Racial discrimination in the British labour market

The black and Asian population remains small in relation to the total white population, but members of these groups continue to be concentrated in inner-city areas and in low-paid work.

There are just over one million people from an ethnic minority background in Britain and relatively few of these are in well-paid jobs. People from ethnic minorities are more likely to be unemployed than the white population. These unemployment rates cannot be explained by differences in levels of qualifications, instead they reflect employer discrimination against ethnic minorities. Is there under-representation of ethnic minorities in social care employment?

ACTIVITY

Has the college you attend or the place where you work an equal opportunities policy? To answer this question talk to the Student Union representative or a senior member of staff responsible for equal opportunities. Find out how the policy is monitored.

Racial groups and old age

What social care problems may older members of ethnic groups experience? For the majority of older people from ethnic groups Britain is a second home rather than their country of birth. For the elderly, their expectations of old age were shaped in other countries where the lifestyles and status of the elderly differ from that in Britain. As a result, in addition to the usual losses experienced in old age, the elderly may feel the loss of the role they would have expected to occupy had they remained in their local communities. Their experience and knowledge would have been highly valued and they would not have been expected to 'retire' at 60 or 65. Instead, their social status would increase with age and they would not be seen as a separate group, but as a useful part of the family and society. They would have remained involved in most spheres of life in their local community.

Britain's welfare services tend to assume that the clients they cater for all have the same needs and experiences. The elderly, along with other groups, encounter prejudice, hostility, stereotyping and discrimination – in other words racism – in their attempts to obtain services. Black elderly people are at the back of the queue for services such as housing. Many live in rented accommodation of a very low standard and in conditions which result from poverty.

ACTIVITY

Devise a diet for an elderly person from a chosen ethnic group.
Discuss your diet with your class and tutor.

ASSIGNMENT 3

The purpose of this assignment is to help you differentiate between the needs of clients who are living in their own homes, sheltered housing or homes for the elderly.

As a class, form into three groups. Each group must select a number of elderly people living in one of the situations described above.

1 Draw up a questionnaire to obtain information from the people interviewed. Information you may wish to obtain could cover:
   - age;
   - marital status;
   - dependency level;
   - ability to shop;
   - ability to go out visiting;
   - the individual's wishes as to where they would like to live.

2 Each group should then write up its findings.

3 Finally, discuss your findings with the other groups.

4 *Health promotion and care*

AIMS

▶ To examine the beneficial effects of a good diet, regular exercise and rest.

▶ To look at the ways of reducing and managing stress.

▶ To understand how our present-day healthcare system has developed.

INTRODUCTION

Health – it's a gift! The value of the gift, however, is seldom realised until it is no longer there. But what is good health?

ACTIVITY

What do you think being healthy means?
Some people appear very healthy and yet may be quite unfit. Others look almost ill and run marathons regularly.

1 In small groups, discuss what being healthy means to you. Record your comments and then share them with the rest of the group.

2 Once you have established some of your own ideas, consider what being healthy might mean to the following people:
a) A middle-aged business person.
b) A keen marathon runner.
c) A parent at home with three children under five years old.
d) A young person recently confined to a wheelchair.
e) A boutique owner who drinks over five bottles of wine per week.
f) A journalist who smokes over 20 cigarettes a day.

One of the conclusions you may reach from doing the above activity is that being healthy is closely linked to what you do and the habits you may develop.

HEALTH MAINTENANCE

This section deals with four aspects of health maintenance: food, exercise, sleep and stress management.

Food for health

Does it matter what we eat?

If we want to feel well, stay fit, have good teeth and keep our weight in proportion to our size, then we need to think about the foods that we eat. It is possible to eat nothing but biscuits, chocolates, snack foods and cakes for a day or two without feeling too many ill effects. However, if we continued with this type of diet for a longer period we would begin to put on weight, be at greater risk from dental caries and generally feel less fit.

The effects of eating the wrong types of food

In Britain, many people suffer from illnesses that can be linked to the diet that they eat. Obesity, anaemia and tooth decay are all linked to poor diets. What you eat now may not affect you immediately, but later in life you may suffer from heart disease, osteoporosis and other illnesses related to malnourishment.

In Britain, one problem is not a shortage of food, but usually too much of the wrong types. Today's lifestyles could make us rely on 'fast foods' or 'junk foods' which contain high levels of the nutrients which make us overweight. However, the choice of foods now available in the shops make healthy eating for all of us much simpler, if we have a basic understanding of what we should eat.

The current recommendations for a healthy diet include:

- eating more fibre;
- eating less sugar;
- eating less fat.

All of these recommendations could be implemented by simple changes in our daily diet.

 ACTIVITY

1 Keep a record over three days of all that you eat and drink.

2 Interview an elderly person and find out what they normally eat and drink.

What are the differences between the two eating habits? What do you think are the reasons for this?

The basic nutrients

Each nutrient has a particular part to play in the body's function. Various nutrients in different foods are all necessary to keep the body in good working order. Foods from each of the following groups must be eaten to make sure that each nutrient is included.

Protein This is needed for the growth and repair of body tissues. It is found mainly in meat, fish, eggs, milk and cheese. Vegetarians obtain most of their protein from soya products, nuts, cereals, peas, beans and lentils. The protein allowance should be divided up between all the day's meals. Protein should be eaten with carbohydrates as the body will use proteins to supply energy if it is short of carbohydrates. This is an expensive form of energy and it also deprives the body of its source of nutrients for growth. Proteins cannot be stored by the body and protein-rich foods can be expensive, but it is important that every member of the family should have a regular supply. In particular, children need a large quantity of protein as their bodies are in a period of growth. Adults need a smaller quantity for the repair of tissue.

Carbohydrates These give us energy. The main carbohydrates are the sugar and starches. Cellulose is also a carbohydrate, but it cannot be digested and is used as roughage. Starches are of vegetable origin and contain other useful nutrients. Sugar, however, has no nutritive value other than warmth and energy, so it is the lease useful of fuel foods.

Fats These also provide energy. Fats and oils are obtained from plants and animals and are a very concentrated form of energy. If we eat more fats and carbohydrates than our body needs they are stored and this can lead to obesity. The main fats in our diet may include butter, margarine, lard, vegetable oils and cream.

Minerals This is a large group of nutrients but we only need them in very small quantities. Some are known as *trace elements* because they are needed in such small quantities. The most important ones are:

- iron, which helps to prevent anaemia. This is found particularly in liver and kidney, dried fruits, eggs, spinach and cocoa.
- calcium and phosphorus, which give us strong bones and teeth. Main sources are cheese, milk and flour.
- iodine, which is necessary for the proper functioning of the thyroid gland. Lack of iodine could lead to a disease known as goitre. Main sources are fish and water.
- sodium chloride which is found in all body fluids. It helps in the function of muscles and a lack of sodium chloride will cause cramp. Mainly found in salt, cheese, kippers, ham and bacon.

Vitamins The four main vitamins which need to be remembered are only available in a limited number of foods. Lack of any vitamin will cause ill health and in serious cases this could lead to disease and even death.

Vitamins are divided into two main groups:

- vitamins A and D are fat-soluble and are generally found in fatty foods.
- vitamins B and C are water-soluble, cannot be stored by the body and therefore daily supplies are needed.

60

Vitamin A is sometimes known as the *anti-infective vitamin* and can be stored by the body to be used when needed. It is found mainly in dairy products, egg yolk, fatty fish and fish liver oils. A secondary source can also be found in orange, yellow or green plants containing carotene, such as carrots and green cabbage. Vitamin A is used by the body to aid growth in children; it helps our eyes to see in dim light; protects our skin; and keeps the lining of the throat, lungs and stomach moist.

Vitamin D is often known as the sunshine vitamin and like vitamin A can also be stored by the body. It is found in fish liver oils, margarine, butter, cheese and eggs. It is important in the formation of strong bones and teeth, and promotes growth. This vitamin can also be made by the body itself by the action of sunlight on the skin.

The vitamin B group contains a number of vitamins, all of which are water-soluble:

- Thiamine is found in brown flour, potatoes, vegetables, meat and yeast. Its main use is in the release of energy from carbohydrate foods as well as maintaining the nervous system and helping in growth. Lack of this vitamin can cause depression and tiredness. Severe lack can cause diseases of the nervous system.
- Riboflavin can be found in eggs, cheese, milk, liver and yeast products. It plays a role in the growth of children, keeps the mouth and tongue free from infection and keeps the cornea of the eye clear.
- Nicotinic acid, sometimes called niacin, is found in bread, cereals, flour, meat and potatoes. Again it is necessary for the growth of children and prevents digestive disorders. Severe lack of this vitamin sometimes occurs in famine areas causing pellagra (a deadly disease).

Vitamin C or ascorbic acid is water-soluble so daily supplies are needed. It is found in citrus fruits, blackcurrants, rose hips, green vegetables and tomatoes. It helps the body resist infection, keeps gums healthy, helps wounds and fractures to heal and ensures a healthy skin. Vitamin C is the vitamin most likely to be lacking in the British diet. Prolonged lack of vitamin C can cause scurvy. It is very easily lost from food in storage and during cooking. You can only ensure that there is sufficient in the diet by:

- using fruit and vegetables in as fresh a state as possible;
- serving fruits and vegetables raw whenever possible;
- keeping cooking times to a minimum;
- dishing up and serving food immediately;
- using the cooking water (stock) which contains dissolved vitamins for making gravy or sauces.

Water This is not usually regarded as a food, but it is important in the diet. Every part and function of the body depends on water and it is being lost continuously through the skin, lungs, kidneys and bowels. This water must be replaced and is obtained from the liquids that we drink and the food that we eat.

ACTIVITY

1 What are nutrients?

2 Name some inexpensive foods which contain several different nutrients.

3 What do you understand by the term 'a balanced diet'?

Planning meals

There is no point in knowing about nutrients if we do not put that knowledge into practice. Before you plan to eat you should consider these questions:

- What pattern of eating suits your way of living?
- What foods are available and what can you afford?
- Is there anyone in your family who has special dietary needs?
- How do you ensure that you obtain the necessary nutrients?

The nutrient triangle

Most of us prepare meals without really thinking about their nutritive value, but more about the likes and dislikes of the people who will be eating the meal. Whilst we want to avoid food being wasted it is important to include foods in each meal that satisfy our dietary needs. No matter what race or culture we belong to it is possible to provide meals that are healthy and satisfy the family's likes and dislikes.

If you divide the main nutrients into three groups then the triangle that they form can be used to check if the meal you are planning is balanced.

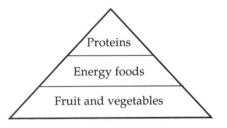

Remember that too many energy foods can cause obesity and that fruit and vegetables should be used to supply the bulk of fibre in our diet.

Different energy requirements

Different people need different amounts of food each day. The amount needed depends on age, sex, size and activity. People with high energy needs, such as children, manual workers and teenagers, will need more energy than less-active people. Sedentary people may need to cut down on energy foods.

ACTIVITY

1 Plan two days' meals for yourself and a friend. How have you ensured that you are getting the right amounts of nutrients?

2 Plan two days' meals for someone with particular dietary needs. (He or she could be elderly/vegetarian/of a different cultural background.) How have you ensured that his or her dietary needs are being met?

EXERCISE FOR HEALTH

For some people, the mere mention of the word 'exercise' makes them shrink away. This reaction may be the result of an accumulation of unhappy experiences relating to exercise and particularly competitive sport. Exercise, however, is an extremely individual matter. People can select from a whole range of exercise patterns and sports to find something which suits their level and their lifestyle.

Look at the drawings in the picture below.

▲ *The benefits of regular exercise*

Check if there is anyone in the group who can verify one or more of these points. Ask them how they feel about exercise.

What are the benefits of exercise?

If you try you will enjoy exercise. You will also feel better for it – eventually! Even if you have exercised regularly, it is easy to lose the habit, particularly if you have just embarked on a new course and changed your social environment.

Regular exercise

If you exercise vigorously but spasmodically, you are shocking your body into action and your muscles are jolted into performance. If you exercise gradually at first and then build up regularly, your body becomes accustomed to the pressure. Limbs become more flexible and your heart and lungs increase their capacity to supply the body with its extra demands for oxygen.

You are less likely to maintain an exercise plan if it is not suited to your life-style.

It is far better to set yourself realistic targets which you know you can fit into your routine – like running a couple of miles before tea or before dark, twice a week – than a time-consuming or expensive sport. It is better for your self-esteem to keep to a regular exercise pattern than to start and then trail off.

Exercise routines

Exercise routines can be divided into two types:

- *Aerobic* – this is exercise which works your heart, lungs and blood system. Running, fast swimming and fast cycling are examples of an aerobic type of exercise.
- *Anaerobic* – this is exercise which concentrates on stretching and flexing the muscles. Yoga and general stretch work are examples of an anaerobic type of exercise.

A good exercise programme will combine the two types of exercise depending on individual needs.

Table 4.1 illustrates the different benefits from various physical activities. Bear in mind, however, that the actual benefits will depend on how vigorously the activity is carried out.

Activity	Stamina rating	Suppleness rating	Strength rating
Badminton	2	3	2
Canoeing	3	2	3
Climbing stairs	3	1	2
Cricket	1	2	1
Cycling (hard)	4	2	3
Dancing (ballroom)	1	3	1
Dancing (disco)	3	4	1
Football	3	3	3
Golf	1	2	1
Gymnastics	2	4	3
Hillwalking	3	1	2
Jogging	4	2	2
Judo	2	4	2
Rowing	4	2	4
Sailing	1	2	2
Squash	3	3	2
Swimming (hard)	4	4	4
Tennis	2	3	2
Walking (briskly)	2	1	1
Weightlifting	1	1	4
Yoga	1	4	1

Key:
1 – no real effect
2 – beneficial effect
3 – very good effect
4 – excellent effect

Table 4.1 *Benefits of various physical activities*

Whichever activity you choose, try to build up gradually. To gain and maintain a fitness level you ought to aim for three, 20-minute sessions per week. Exercise which is boring, gruelling or difficult to fit in with your lifestyle will be a problem to maintain. Choose something you feel happy with and which is not too disruptive of your routine at work and home. You may encourage friends and family to join you.

Another point concerning anaerobic work is that some people of average flexibility try to work at levels which are beyond them and injury results.

Try to:

- Warm up thoroughly.
- Avoid jerky movements.
- Avoid exercises which leave the back unsupported like the 'bridge' (Figure 4.1a).
- Take care doing double-leg raises (Figure 4.1b) or exercises which involve lifting the leg high to a fixed point (Figure 4.1c).
- Be cautious doing sit-ups with straight legs (Figure 4.1d).

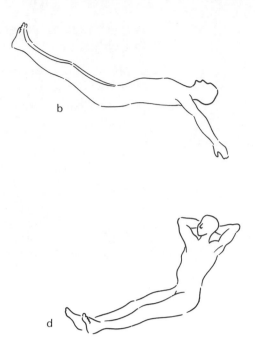

▲ *Figure 4.1 Take care when doing various exercises*

Questions to consider before exercise

- Can you afford the cost of the exercise?
- Are you fit or do you need a medical check-up?
- Do you have suitable clothes?
- Do you have suitable footwear?
- Is the weather suitable and safe for the exercise?
- Do you have enough time to warm up before and cool down after?
- Have you eaten enough and sufficiently early so that the food is digested?

Monitoring exercise

You will find it encouraging to monitor your progress in terms of how fit you are getting during the training programme.

Pulse rate

Taking your pulse is one way of monitoring your fitness. The slower your pulse the fitter you are getting.

To check your pulse, press the artery on the inside of your wrist with your first three fingers. Count how many beats you can feel in 10 seconds and then multiply by six; alternatively count the number of beats you can feel in 60 seconds. The average pulse rate is about 70 beats per minute.

Now that you can check your pulse try a few exercises to monitor your fitness level:

- Walk up and down a flight of steps, say 15 to 20 in total. On the whole, if you are more than mildly breathless and your pulse rate is higher than average then you may be unfit.
- Run on the spot for about three minutes. If your pulse is over 90 and you are mildly breathless then you are fairly unfit.

- Using a firm bench or the second step of a stair, step up and down briskly. Aim for about two steps up and down every six seconds for about three minutes. If you are very breathless and your pulse rate is above 90 then you are pretty unfit.
- Jog gently for about one mile. This should take about 10 minutes. If you are not breathless then you are fairly fit.

Useful exercises for carers

Caring can be a hectic and stressful occupation. You are often on your feet for long hours. There is a temptation when you are very busy to rush your meals and to slump down in the first chair you see when you have finished work. A more beneficial habit would be to lie flat on the floor or bed with your feet slightly raised.

Stretching and flexing exercises

Remember to warm up thoroughly before you begin any stretching or flexing. You can do this by running on the spot for two minutes or skipping if you have room.

1 Start with some head rolls to loosen neck and shoulder muscles. Stand with feet apart, shoulders dropped and then roll the head round six times one way and six times the other.
2 Turn head three times to the left and three to the right. Drop head forward – chin on chest three times.
3 Hunch right shoulder to ear and drop three times. Same for left and then both together.
4 Strong abdominal muscles are important – this exercise helps.
   - lie flat on the floor;
   - raise knees;
   - feet flat on the floor;
   - slowly lift up through a rounded spine so that hands go just above the knees.

   Try four of these at first and then hug your knees to your chest. Then try a further four. Try to work towards six continual raises. Go slowly. Do *not* jerk. Breathe in as you go down and out as you come up
5 Still on the floor, raise yourself onto your elbows and cycle your legs forward. Work towards 12 pedals and then hug your knees in.
6 For back strength. Lie on your tummy. Raise one leg straight behind you and hold for a count of two. Then raise the other leg and hold for a count of two. Finally, raise both legs for a count of two. Eventually try to work to holding both legs to a count of four.
7 For general flexibility try side bends. Stand legs apart with hands on hips. Bend eight times to the right and eight times to the left.
8 Same as 7 but this time with hands behind the head.
9 Same position, but slide your right arm down the right leg. Repeat for the left.
10 Body bender. Stand with feet apart. Raise your arms above your head and then swoop round in a big circle around your own body. First clockwise and the anti-clockwise.
11 Lie on your side with both legs stretched out. Raise the top leg eight times. Then swing the leg in front and behind the body eight times. Change legs.
12 Relaxation position. Lie flat on tummy, arms stretched out in front, and head facing down. Draw the knees up and you should feel a good stretch in the spine. Arch and then drop the back like a cat three times.

SLEEP AND REST

No one is quite sure about how much sleep people need. Certainly young people need more than the average, but individuals vary. Are you aware of your own sleep needs and patterns? Lack of sleep affects your ability to concentrate; you may, as a result, feel less ready to cope with the demands of the day.

What happens when you sleep?

During sleep the body repairs itself. The growth hormone is released and enters the blood stream. This stimulates the various tissues and organs of the body to repair themselves and grow. Even the brain grows and repairs itself during sleep.

In addition to the growth and repair process phase of sleep, you also experience another type of sleep termed REM (Rapid Eye Movement) sleep. This is when your eyes actually make rapid movements and your electric brain waves are faster than in ordinary sleep. If you are woken during this period of sleep you can often remember your dreams.

During the day the two sides (hemispheres) of the brain are usually active so that you can respond to what is going on around you. The amount of activity in your brain depends on the stimulation that comes from the brain stem. The brain stem lies at the point where the brain is attached to the spinal cord. If there is little stimulation the activity in the brain hemispheres declines and you can drift off to sleep.

The brain stem actually works on a 24-hour cycle of activity. You may be one of those people who go to bed late and have a 25-hour cycle. Others may be early to bed – a 23-hour cycle. If you are excited or worried the brain stem is stimulated by the hemispheres so that it becomes difficult to relax and wind down.

What happens when you can't sleep?

One of the best ways of getting a good night's sleep is to take some exercise, particularly outdoor exercise like walking or running. Being physically worn out often forces you to relax.

Sometimes people find it extremely difficult to sleep because of a personal crisis. They may become depressed and unable to sleep for a period. A doctor may prescribe a sleeping tablet, but this should never be a first choice. Natural sleep is always the best and it is worth trying all the 'common sense' measures, like milky drinks and exercise, before resorting to medication.

Sleeping tablets

A sleeping tablet depresses the activity of the brain stem and relieves anxieties to induce sleep. However, it reduces the amount of time spent dreaming and reduces the intensity of the dreams. When the sleeping tablets are reduced and stopped, the dreams become very vivid and it may take up to two months for the sleep pattern to return to normal.

Another adverse effect of sleeping tablets is the continuing presence they may have the next day, so that it becomes difficult to be alert and concentrate.

A final note – barbiturate sleeping tablets are no longer prescribed. They are addictive and *very* dangerous, especially if combined with alcohol.

Monitor and record your sleep pattern for a week. Note how you react if you do not get enough sleep.

STRESS

Most people are aware that too much stress can endanger your health, but too little stress can also be bad for you. People who have few demands made on them or who have little stimulation may find themselves feeling very tired without doing very much or wanting to do very much. Some people thrive on stress, but others find even a minimal disruption difficult to cope with.

Defining stress

Stress is a response. It is the imbalance between an individual and the demands made of that individual. The term *stressor* is used to describe the demand. This could be a noise, a task or a thought which makes the demand that produces a stress response in the individual.

An extreme and sudden stress produces a physical reaction. For example, if you think a child is about to run out in front of a car:

- Your eyes and ears receive an alarm signal.
- Your brain registers the child is in danger and sends messages out along the nerves.
- Your muscles contract in readiness for action.
- The strength of your heart beat increases so blood is pumped more quickly to where it is most needed, i.e. your muscles.

- Chemicals in the brain set off a number of hormonal changes in your body. Adrenalin is produced.
- Your hearing becomes more sensitive.
- Your skin goes pale because the blood has to go elsewhere.
- Your breathing gets faster.
- Your blood pressure rises, carrying oxygen more quickly to the heart, muscles and brain.
- Your sweating increases.
- You may be left feeling faint because the fear causes you to breathe too fast, leading to less blood in the brain.

Interestingly, a similar physical reaction may be felt if somebody you feel quite strongly about actually enters the room where you are.

Reaction to stress

People may react differently to stress or have different reactions at different times. For example, if you are engrossed in a piece of work and some friends call round then you might take a *fight response*. You throw down your pen, open the door muttering irritably and announce that you are busy. Or you may think to yourself that you will take a break and put the kettle on thus adopting a *flight response*.

People who use the fight response tend to be conscientious types who work hard and find it difficult to relax. Sometimes people actually suppress the fight response so that they appear to be calm and in control, but in fact they are seething within.

People who adopt the flight response are trying to escape from stressful situations. These people tend to be more cautious. They may withdraw from stressful situations and pass up opportunities for advancement.

It is not that one particular reaction is better than another. Over-use of one particular response, however, may lead to a fixed, rigid pattern and eventually a stressed state.

The *flow response*, which is neither fighting nor running away, is an attempt to go with whatever the current trend happens to be. These people usually stay fairly cool. Such people can be viewed as erratic and with no fixed values, but are very tolerant.

Obviously, the types outlined are broad stereotypes and many people fall between these categories, or may vary from one type to another.

ACTIVITY

Think of something which might cause you stress in the next week and try to monitor your own response to it.

Did you fight or run away? Why? On reflection, do you think that was the best reaction to the situation?

Causes of stress

Stress is a highly individual matter. Different things cause stress levels in different people. Noisy or hazardous environments, relationships or work may all be stressful. Experts acknowledge that major life changes are generally stressful. The quiz in the Activity opposite gives crisis ratings for various life events. The higher your score, the more stressful the past two years have been for you.

Life changes and stress

Make a note of the numbers, if the events have happened to you in the last two years, and then add up your score.

Life event (in last two years)	Crisis unit	Score
Death of spouse or partner	100	_____
Divorce	73	_____
Marital separation	65	_____
Jail term	63	_____
Death of close family member	63	_____
Personal injury or illness	53	_____
Marriage	50	_____
Fired at work	47	_____
Made redundant	45	_____
Marital reconciliation	45	_____
Retirement	45	_____
Pregnancy	40	_____
Change of health of family member	39	_____
Sex difficulties	39	_____
Gain of new family member	39	_____
Business readjustment	39	_____
Change in financial state	38	_____
Death of close friend	37	_____
Change to a different line of work	36	_____
Change in number of arguments with spouse or partner	35	_____
Mortgage over £10,000	31	_____
Foreclosure of mortgage or loan	30	_____
Change in responsibilities at work	29	_____
Son or daughter leaving home	29	_____
Trouble with in-laws	29	_____
Outstanding personal achievement	28	_____
Wife or female partner begins or stops work	26	_____
Begin or end school	26	_____
Change in living conditions	25	_____
Revision of personal habits	24	
Trouble with boss at work	23	
Change in work hours or conditions	23	_____
Change in residence	20	_____
Change in school	20	_____
Change in recreation	19	_____
Change in religious activities	19	_____
Change in social activities	18	_____
Mortgage or loan less than £10,000	17	_____
Change in sleeping habits	16	_____
Change in number of family get-togethers	15	
Change in eating habits	15	_____
Holiday	15	_____
Minor violation of the law	11	_____

Stress at work

The people who experience stress are not always the stereotyped top managers. Shift work can be stressful. Manual jobs may involve working with physical and chemical hazards. Safety measures may make it difficult to have working relationships; for example, it is difficult to have any sort of conversation if you have to wear ear muffs or indeed if factory or construction site noise levels are high.

Another cause of stress at work is relationships. Sometimes seniors may exert unreasonable pressure to achieve tasks in unreasonable deadlines.

Below are listed some of the factors people find stressful about work and which may be very difficult to cope with.

- **Money worries**   Your income is low. You cannot earn more. Your job is not secure.
- **Relationships**   You do not get on well with some or all of your colleagues. You are forced to work with people you do not like.
- **Poor working conditions**   You have to put up with noise, vibration, poor lighting, heat, cold, poor ventilation, danger from physical or chemical hazards, fear of accidents, dirt and grime, long hours of overtime and shiftwork.
- **Poor administration and company policy**   You get a lot of bother from inefficient administration.
- **Work load**   You have too much responsibility or work to handle or not enough work or responsibility.
- **Prospects**   There is no hope of promotion or advancement.
- **Recognition**   No one appreciates what you do.
- **Satisfaction**   The job is boring and you have too much time on your hands or so demanding you have no time left for yourself.
- **Goals**   You do not feel you can ever achieve or finish anything because the demands are constantly changing.

Signs of stress in the workplace
- High turnover of staff.
- High absenteeism.
- High illness rates.
- High strike rates.
- High accident rates.

If a job has satisfaction and meaning to those who do it, and if there is pride in the work, then the turnover rates, absenteeism, illness, strike and accident rates are all low. Studies in Sweden have shown that where workers can arrange their own schedules in consultation with a foreman rather than doing the same job over and over again, there is far greater interest and satisfaction in the work. Control and variety can also lead to higher standards of work.

The symptoms and results of stress

Extreme stress can cause ill health, but remember that people have differing stress tolerances and that stress can be prevented and managed.

The lists below show some of the symptoms of stress.

Physical symptoms
These can include any of the following:

- Tension in the muscular system, in the back of the neck or lower back. Headaches may be the result of this increased muscular tension.
- Nausea (feeling sick).
- Tension in the jaw – grinding teeth.
- Diaphragm and pelvic muscles often tense up.
- Throat muscles change leading to changes in voice or nervous laughter
- If the muscle tension is severe this can lead to blinking, nervous tics, trembling and shaking.

- Raised blood pressure.
- Disorders of the glandular system including excessive sweating, dry throat and difficulty in swallowing.
- Heart and lungs are affected resulting in rapid pulse rates, a pounding heart and rapid, shallow breathing.
- The nervous system is affected, resulting in dizziness, fainting spells, weakness, lethargy and difficulty in sleeping, too much sleep or disturbed sleep.

Psychological symptoms

These can include any of the following:

- Inability to concentrate.
- General irritability.
- Being over-exact.
- Sense of mild fear or panic.
- Inability to enjoy yourself.
- Inattention to hygiene or dress.
- General dullness and flatness.
- Emotional and social withdrawal.
- Poor work performance.
- Difficulty in communicating.
- Loss of sex drive.

Stress management

What can be done to reduce stress? There are many aspects of stress management, but the first is to be aware of your own stresses and reactions to them.

ACTIVITY

In pairs, work through the interview questions below. One person should be the interviewer and the other the interviewee (the person being asked the questions). You could then swop places if you have time.

Interview

The interviewer asks the following questions.

1 Think about something that happened to you that was a very stressful experience for you. Tell me about it.

2 Was this experience something you knew was going to happen or was it a surprise to you?

3 What did you feel when this happened and what did you do?

4 Can you remember doing anything that made you feel any better or less anxious?

5 Did you turn to anyone else for help? What happened?

6 If you had to face this experience again would you do anything different the second time? Could you have done anything to prevent this experience happening or that would have made it less stressful for you?

7 Did you learn anything about yourself as a result of the experience?

8 What factors do you generally find stressful?

9 What helps you to cope with these factors?

Stress management techniques

The key to managing stress is to consider three important areas. These are:

- physical fitness;
- good diet;
- time management.

The first two are concerned with your physical well-being. *Time management* is being aware of how you spend your time. Can you alter your life to relieve certain pressures at busy times? Being organised about your time avoids leaving things to the last minute. There are certain aspects of stress management:

- assertiveness – saying 'No' without feeling guilty.
- meditation;
- relaxation;
- massage;
- emotional release, such as tears or talking;
- self-talk and positive thinking – telling yourself to treat each situation as positively as possible;
- communication skills, for example, talking through your problems with a friend or counsellor;
- support systems – using friends and family or more formal guidance and counselling systems.

ACTIVITY

1 Consider the above list of stress management techniques. See which ones might suit you.

2 Choose one technique and research it further.

3 As a class, discuss a possible design and format for a booklet entitled 'Dealing with Stress'.

4 The individual pieces of research could be collated and presented in the form of bar charts using the computer.

Some tips for stress survival

- Do one thing at a time.
- Find a quiet nook at home to be by yourself.
- Do not rush.
- Eat well and enjoy your food.
- Listen, do not interrupt.
- Plan a treat for yourself.

ACTIVITY

What is health?

Most of us can say what it is to be unwell, but can you define what it means to be healthy? Being healthy means different things to different people. This activity will enable you to compare what being healthy means to you and will allow you to discuss your definitions with your colleagues.

1 Split into pairs and complete the following check-list. Tick the statements that you agree with.

Being healthy is:	Me	Partner
Feeling well		
Living to be old		
Able to take part in games		
Being the right weight for body type		
Being fit		
Never smoking		
Never suffering illness		
Feeling good		
Not suffering from stress		
Enjoying my job		
Eating the right food		
Never drinking		
Never going to the doctor		
List others you may think of:		
_____		
_____		

2 Compare your list with others in the group.

3 What can you do to keep healthy? Write some guidelines for a new student starting a course and living away from home for the first time.

HEALTH CARE

We may well work hard at maintaining our health and avoiding damaging habits, but there are times when medical treatment is necessary. In Britain, in the 1990s, we have a system of free health care. Health care, however, has not always been free and indeed some people today choose to pay into private health care schemes to avoid National Health Service (NHS) waiting lists. But what is the NHS and how does it work?

In 1948, a Labour Minister for Health, Aneurin Bevan, set up a health service on a national basis. Before 1948, all doctors worked privately and people had to pay to see them for treatment. If people needed hospital treatment then they had to go into one of the three types of hospital:

- local authority hospitals;
- voluntary hospitals;
- cottage hospitals.

Local authority hospitals

These were hospitals which the local authority had to set up by law. If people had mental health problems then they may have been admitted to an 'asylum', as they were then called. If a person had an infectious illness, such as TB, then they would go to a sanatorium or isolation hospital. People who were poor and in need of hospital care went to 'workhouse hospitals'. Conditions in workhouse hospitals were very bad and people feared them. Thus the local authority provided:

Local authority
Asylums   Isolation   Workhouse
               hospitals   hospitals

Voluntary hospitals

These hospitals had much better conditions. People raised funds or donated money to build and maintain them. Some hospitals still have the names of the people who gave a lot of money to establish them. Some older hospitals may have wards named after people who donated money and sometimes there are plaques above beds bearing the names of donors. Doctors worked in the voluntary hospitals for less pay and some ran their own private practices to compensate. People paid for their treatment according to how much they could afford. Many people took out insurance schemes to help financially in the case of illness.

Cottage hospitals

Cottage hospitals were smaller and based in rural settings. The doctors who treated patients at their surgeries would also treat them in the hospitals, if they needed to be admitted.

Other health benefits

In 1948, Bevan also arranged that prescriptions, glasses, hearing aids and dentures could all be claimed free of charge. It was as though a miracle had happened for some who for years could not hear or see properly.

The cost of this National Health Service was enormous and later charges had to be introduced for prescriptions, glasses, hearing aids and dentures.

Development of the present-day NHS

The structure which Bevan set up to run the NHS consisted of Regional Hospital Boards that took orders from central government. They controlled the finance of the hospitals within the region and issued instructions to Hospital Management Committees. These in turn took care of the day-to-day management of the hospitals.

The Local Authorities retained their responsibilities for community services like home nursing and health education. General Practitioners (GPs) were organised through Family Practitioner Committees.

ACTIVITY

1 Arrange to talk to an elderly person about health care before the NHS. Hold a group session where you can exchange accounts.

2 Use the local history section of a main library and try to check out the beginnings of three hospitals in your area.

The structure which Bevan imposed in 1948 remained largely unchanged until 1974. In 1974, the system was reorganised to try to create a more integrated or unified approach to care.

Before 1974 there were three arms to the NHS:

- GPs under Family Practitioner Committees;
- hospitals under Hospital Management Committees;
- Local Authority Services.

There are a number of reasons why it was thought necessary to reorganise the services:

- community services were underused;
- with the number of elderly people increasing it was felt that they would benefit more from community services as opposed to being in hospital;
- other groups would also benefit from more continuous care; for example, pregnant women, young children and people with special needs;
- there was very little continuous care; people had to deal with separate organisations.

In an attempt to try to solve some of these problems, the Regional Hospital Boards became Regional Health Authorities and the Hospital Management Committees became Area Health Authorities. The Area Health Authorities took over the running of community health services, including school health, but social work, home helps and non-medical services for the elderly remained under Local Authority control.

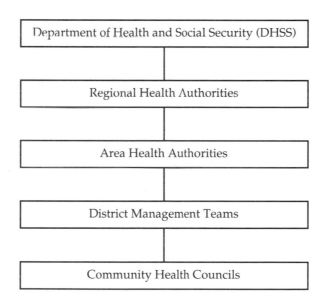

▲ *Figure 4.2 Structure of the NHS in 1974*

In 1974, the District Management Teams took care of units within the area (see Figure 4.2). In Sheffield, for example, there were three smaller units – Central, Northern and Southern. Community Health Councils were set up to represent the community's point of view in the structure.

In 1981, the Area Health Authorities were thought to be costly and less useful, so Area Health Authorities became District Health Authorities and the structure changed again (see Figure 4.3).

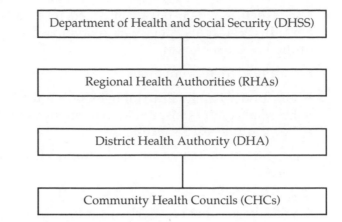

▲ *Figure 4.3 Structure of the NHS in 1981*

In 1984, Primary Health Care Teams were introduced. These are multi-disciplinary teams, that is teams with a range of expertise and medical personnel, supported by receptionists.

By 1989 the structure of the NHS looked like that in Figure 4.4. Community Health Councils are not featured in the diagram because they are independent of the formal NHS structure. Each NHS district has a Community Health Council with members appointed by the Local Authority, voluntary groups and the Regional Health Authority. Their job is to represent the interests of the patients and the District Health Authority has to consult them over any closures. Council members have the right to visit NHS buildings and talk to senior district officers.

In 1990, the National Health Service Community Care Act aimed to prevent ill health and promote good health. Through the Act, GPs are encouraged to set up 'Life Style Check Ups'. You may have noticed 'Well Man' or 'Well Woman' clinics at your own GP's surgery. Such clinics are designed to give people the chance to discuss anything that worries them, to have routine checks, like blood pressure, and to provide advice on matters like exercise and diet.

GPs are also encouraged to offer Family Planning Services. If you do not want to see your own GP about family planning, then you can see another *if* the other GP is willing to accept you.

More information is now available to help you find out about the services doctors provide. Family Practitioner Committees now produce directories of local family doctors giving information about each doctor and the services provided. GPs themselves are also producing leaflets about the range of their services.

Changing to another GP is easier now. If you want to go to a different GP then all you have to do is turn up at the surgery of the doctor of your choice and ask to be registered. If your new doctor agrees to put you on his or her list then that is all that is required.

From April 1991, larger practices or health centres will be able to take control of some NHS funds to finance the services for their own patients. These include certain hospital treatments, prescriptions and staff. The level of the funds will be agreed between the GP and the RHA and it will take into account the health needs of the community.

The same applies to some hospitals. Certain hospitals have opted to manage their own budgets which come directly from the government. The hospital can use the budget how they think best within the hospital. Some people have criticised this self-management, fearing that hospitals may concentrate on those forms of treatment which are less costly in order to remain financially stable.

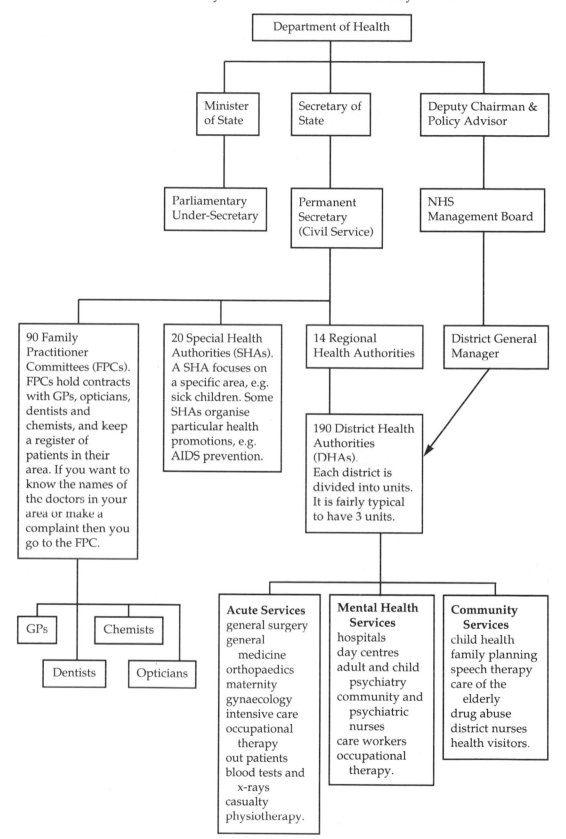

▲ *Figure 4.4 Structure of the NHS in 1989 (England and Wales)*

Make a booklet explaining the health service provision in your area. You may be able to gain some information from your Community Health Council. Include hospitals, GPs, dentists, opticians and health promotion work. Try to find out if there are any facilities for alternative medicine, for example homeopathy.

Work in pairs. Look at the picture below and discuss how the factors in the balloons may affect your health.

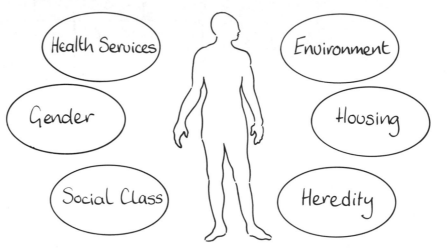

ASSIGNMENT 4

Working in groups of four or five produce a health promotion display for a specific client group

Tasks

1 Select a topic which is relevant to your client group.

2 Research a topic using as many resources as possible.

3 Plan a display, bearing in mind the nature of the client group.

4 Mount the display.

5 Evaluate the display.

6 Take down the display and clear away.

Tips

● Think about your client group carefully and choose a topic which is appropriate and beneficial.

● Use the creative skills of the group to produce a display which is visually stimulating as well as informative.

● Plan the timing of the tasks so that you do not have to rush at the end.

● Research thoroughly, using as many different sources of information as you can.

● Try to work efficiently and co-operatively as a team. You may want to appoint a leader or decide that particular people are responsible for set tasks.

5 *Health risks*

AIMS

▶ To look at the ways in which people can risk damaging their health by smoking, drinking alcohol to excess or using drugs.

▶ To understand the effects of these drugs on the body.

▶ To find out what help is available for the various groups affected.

SMOKING

Most smokers admit that they wish that they had never started to smoke, not least because of the health risks that they face. In fact 100 000 deaths each year are caused by smoking. Particular problems (see Figure 5.1) include:

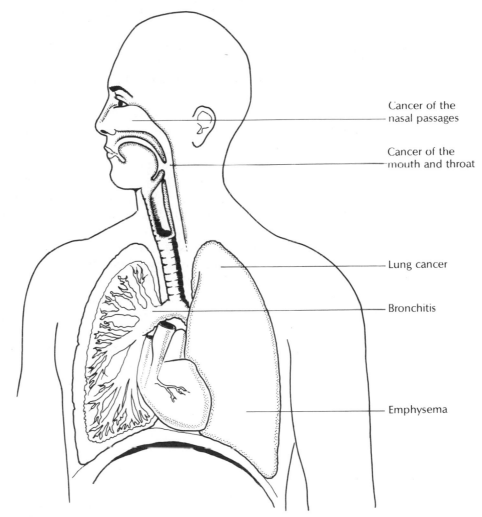

▲ *Figure 5.1 Problems caused by smoking*

- **Lung cancer**   There are 40 000 cases of lung cancer diagnosed in Britain each year. 90 per cent of these cases are caused by smoking and 90 per cent of these people are dead within two years.

  Lung cancer occurs when the lethal cocktail of chemicals in cigarette smoke attacks the genetic material in the lung cells. This causes changes that make the cells multiply wildly so that they collect together. Masses of cells build up and the lungs cannot work.
- **Throat and mouth cancer**   Smokers are four times more at risk from these cancers even if they do not inhale.
- **Bronchitis**   This is a serious inflammation of the tubes leading to the lungs. The tubes become blocked by a jelly-like mucus and then the damaged tissue is easily infected by bacteria. Bronchitis can also affect non-smokers, but it is more common and worse in smokers.
- **Emphysema**   This is caused by the destruction of the feathery branches deep in the lungs. People suffering from the condition are initially short of breath, but eventually so dependent on oxygen supplies that they can hardly move outside their own home. Nine out of ten cases of emphysema are caused by smoking.
- **Hardening of the arteries**   Another condition associated with heavy smoking is the 'furring up' of the arteries. This makes it extremely painful to walk and can lead to amputation of limbs.

  Arteries are the tubes that carry blood from the heart. The tubes become 'furred up' when fatty deposits, caused by factors such as smoking and high blood cholestrol, collect. These fatty deposits are called *atheroma*. The presence of atheroma makes it harder to pump blood through the tubes and limits the amount of oxygen that can be carried around the body. The narrowing of the heart's own arteries can result in severe chest pain. A heart attack occurs when one of the arteries is completely blocked by a blood clot and this can kill.
- **Heart disease**   The specific ways in which smoking promotes heart disease are not certain. Nicotine may be involved because it makes the heart beat faster and therefore the heart's requirement for oxygen is greater. It also makes the blood stickier and harder to pump.

  Smokers also take in carbon monoxide which reduces the oxygen-carrying capacity of a smoker's blood by as much as 15 per cent. In an attempt to compensate for this loss, the body produces extra haemoglobin which means the the blood becomes more likely to clot. Carbon monoxide also contributes to the hardening of the arteries.

  So, smoking goads the heart to beat faster while making the blood harder to pump, more likely to clot and less likely to carry oxygen.
- **Post-operative complications**   Because of the extra pressure smokers place on the heart they run greater risks during and after surgery.
- **Cervical cancer**   Woman smokers run twice the risk of cervical cancer than women non-smokers.
- **Miscarriage**   Pregnant women, even those smoking less than 20 cigarettes per day, are 20 per cent more likely to miscarry. Premature births and stillbirths are also more common amongst smokers than non-smokers. The same is true for infertility.
- **Gum disease**   Smokers are more likely to have gum disease and consequently dental problems.

Passive smoking

The health risks from smoking are undoubtedly heavy. The risks of ill health, however, are also run by other people in terms of *passive smoking*. People who live or work in smoky atmospheres without smoking themselves are termed *passive smokers*. They are vulnerable to the same diseases, as explained above, but to a lesser extent. It is very difficult to estimate the risk of passive smoking, but two studies of children with parents who both smoked estimated that the children breathed in the equivalent amount of smoke as that associated with actively smoking 80–150 cigarettes per year.

Passive Smoking **Questions and Answers**

Passive smoking can also aggravate asthma and other bronchial conditions.

Stopping smoking

It is difficult to stop, but if you do then within one year the health risks you run are 50 per cent above non-smokers. After five years of non-smoking you have little more risk of heart disease than a life-long non-smoker.

Another reason for giving up smoking is that it has become an anti-social habit. More and more venues are becoming completely smoke-free or have special smoke-free zones. People generally feel smoking leaves unpleasant smells on clothes, hair and breath. It is no longer considered sophisticated or attractive to smoke.

Finally, smoking is very expensive. It is hard exercise for a smoker to calculate the annual expense of their smoking habit. It is easy too for the smoker to justify the expense by saying that they do without other things in order to afford cigarettes. It does seem ironic, however, to pay for possible damage to your own health.

Smoking is also costly to the community in terms of passive smoking, nursing care and working days lost through ill health caused by smoking. About half the fires dealt with by the fire brigade are caused by smoking. In 1985, the fire at Bradford Football ground, in which 56 people died, was caused by a discarded cigarette. Similarly, in the tragic Kings Cross fire, the dirt and debris in the escalator shafts were ignited by a cigarette.

How to stop

If you are young and only smoke occasionally it is worth noting that many heavy smokers started with an occasional, social smoke, once a week perhaps, but the habit became established and very difficult to break.

As smoking is an addiction rather than just a habit, the smoker must really **want** to stop. It needs a lot of willpower to stop as the smoker will probably feel the effects of withdrawing from the nicotine.

Some people switch to low-tar cigarettes and these do cause less damage. It is difficult, however, for heavy smokers to adjust to the change and some may smoke more because they find the low-tar cigarettes are less satisfying. In some areas, Health Promotion Councils offer group therapy sessions to support people as they give up.

Few people manage to reduce their level of smoking so low that they stop entirely. The temptation is to creep back up gradually. On the other hand, to 'cold turkey' and stop suddenly is very difficult because of the effects of nicotine withdrawal.

In Britain there are 10 million ex-smokers. It is not easy, but it can be done!

ACTIVITY

Discuss the following issues:

1 Is the government doing enough to discourage smoking? (At present there is a partial ban on advertising tobacco products, the famous Government Health Warnings are being displayed and it is illegal for cigarettes to be sold to those under 16 years of age.)

2 Is it true to say that people have a right to enjoy themselves how they wish?

3 More than half the world's tobacco is grown by poor developing nations who desperately need the cash that the tobacco crops bring. Thousands of people in these countries are employed in making and selling tobacco. Is it right that every job in the tobacco manufacturing industry should equal the deaths of five smokers in the Western world each year?

4 Within your own group, ask the smokers how they started and what advice they would give to anyone who is tempted to smoke.

ALCOHOL

Unlike smoking, drinking alcohol is still very socially acceptable. Indeed it is expected that we will drink on certain occasions. To refuse alcohol may seem embarrassing. You may think that people will consider you odd or cranky if you refuse even a mildly-alcoholic drink. It is often overlooked that alcohol is in fact a drug. It is a legal, socially-accepted drug, but one which can cause much personal and social damage. In fact, there are more deaths through excessive drinking than through heroin abuse.

What is alcohol?

Alcohol is formed by the fermentation action of yeasts on various fruits or cereals. The resulting liquid, with various additions, may be drunk as wines or beers. The alcohol may be further concentrated by distilling or boiling off to produce various spirits, such as whisky, gin or vodka. Different drinks contain different amounts of alcohol.

10 grams of pure alcohol, the amount contained in half a pint of beer, is regarded as one unit. This unit measure is the equivalent of one glass of wine or a pub measure of spirits. Table 5.1 lists the unit levels of various alcoholic drinks, but it is important to note that:

- Wines vary a great deal in strength and it is better to check the label than assume a particular unit level.
- There is also a range of strengths in beers from fairly light beers and lagers, at two units per pint, through to stronger ones, such as *Guinness* and *Stella Artois*, which contain three units per pint. Some beers are even stronger.

Drink	Units
1 bottle of spirits	30.0
1 bottle of table wine	10.0–18.0 or 7.0–12.0
1 bottle of sherry/martini/port	14.0
1 can of special lager	4.0
1 bottle of special lager	2.5
1 can of beer	1.5
1 pint of cider	2.0–4.0
1 pint of beer	2.0–3.0
1 glass of wine	1.0–2.0
1 glass of sherry/martini/port	1.0
1 measure ($\frac{1}{6}$ gill) of spirits	1.0

Table 5.1 *Unit levels of various alcoholic drinks*

Alcohol levels

Current advice is that men ought to consume no more than 21 units per week and women no more than 14.

When the police stop drivers suspected of 'driving whilst under the influence of drink', they measure the **B**lood **A**lcohol **C**oncentration – **BAC**. This is the concentration of alcohol in the body's system. It is difficult to state precisely how much drink needs to be consumed in order for a person to be above the legal limit because people have different tolerance levels in relation to alcohol. As a broad rule, one unit of alcohol or half a pint of beer is equivalent to a BAC of 15 mg (milligrams) per 100 ml (millilitres) BAC. The legal limit for driving is 80 mg per 100 ml BAC, so an average-sized man would be around the legal limit for driving if he has drunk five units or 2.5 pints of ordinary beer (or its equivalent). A smaller man or a woman may be above the BAC legal limit by drinking five units of alcohol.

Alcohol concentration in the body

The factors which affect alcohol concentration in the body are:

- the amount of alcohol consumed;
- the size of the drinker;
- the sex of the drinker (women have proportionately less body fluid than men and are therefore less able to absorb alcohol);
- the rate at which drinks are consumed;
- the amount of food in the stomach.

Almost all of the alcohol in a pint of beer is absorbed after one hour if it is drunk on an empty stomach. If there is food in the stomach the alcohol is absorbed more slowly

Most of the alcohol consumed is removed from the body by the liver. A little is eliminated through breathing and urine. On average, one pint of ordinary beer takes about two hours to filter out of the body.

Read the information below concerning Alicia Robson and then plot the graph outlined.

Alicia Robson runs a small boutique. The boutique was a thriving concern but high interest rates have meant that recent months have been more difficult. On Friday evening she arranges a promotion for the boutique to coincide with some new garments arriving from France. It is a cheese and wine celebration. So:

- On Friday evening Alicia drinks five glasses of wine very rapidly.   *5 units*
- On Saturday at lunchtime Alicia meets her boyfriend for a pub lunch. She has half a pint of cider, one sherry and some sandwiches.   *2 units*
- On Saturday evening Alicia goes to a dinner dance. She drinks two gins and four glasses of wine.   *6 units*

Plot the level of her BAC on a graph like the one below.

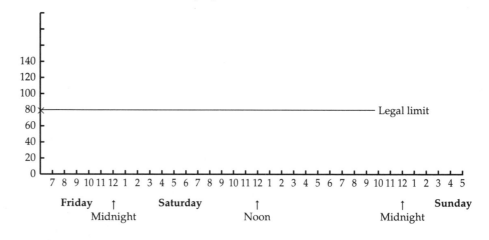

Remember
- One unit of alcohol = 15 mg/100 ml BAC.
- Five units is very near the legal limit.
- Two units of alcohol takes about two hours to filter through the body (rough guide only).

Questions

1 Roughly how long would it take for Alicia to eliminate the alcohol from the cheese and wine celebration on Friday evening?

2 When is Alicia's BAC at its highest?

3 What arrangements might Alicia consider concerning her journeys home on Friday and Saturday nights?

How excessive alcohol consumption affects the body

- Many people turn to drink in times of **stress**. Alcohol is a *depressant* drug which can act as a tranquilliser if amounts below the recommended units are taken. If excess alcohol is taken, however, the nervous system is initially 'weighed down' by the depressant nature of the drug, and then when the effects wear off the nervous system rebounds like a coiled spring. This 'rebound' produces feelings of nervousness, tension and restlessness.

- **Stomach disorders** like gastritis are also common amongst many drinkers. Gastritis is the result of alcohol stripping parts of the stomach of its mucous lining, producing pain and eventually diarrhoea. Peptic ulcers are also associated with prolonged heavy drinking.

- In the short term, alcohol may have a positive effect on **sleep** patterns. In the long term, however, alcohol increases anxiety, depression and therefore insomnia.

- Alcohol also has the effect of suppressing the body's own **immune system** making very heavy drinkers more vulnerable to infection and disease.

- Alcohol stimulates **insulin production** in the pancreas. Insulin reduces sugar levels in the blood and can lead to very low blood sugar counts. Thus the person feels drowsy, weak, trembly and may faint.

- Alcohol can simultaneously **increase weight** and **cause malnutrition**. Alcohol provides calories – one gin and tonic is 150 calories and a pint of beer 300 – but it does *not* provide nutrition. So you can become quite fat but be malnourished. Some drinkers do lose their appetite and excessive drinkers tend to eat very little so they become extremely thin.

  A further point in connection with food and alcohol is that alcohol can stop your body absorbing vitamins. The B vitamins are especially vulnerable and in some cases severe brain damage can result from the deficiency of thiamine (B1).

- The effects of alcohol on the **heart** are complicated. Moderate drinking can lower the risk of heart disease in certain people, but excessive drinking increases the risk.

- Continual excessive drinking may cause inflammation of the **brain**, gradually reducing brain size and resulting in intellectual deterioration. (Note that this is not the same as temporary 'brain muddle' after occasional heavy bouts of drinking.)

- One of the best known conditions associated with heavy drinking is **cirrhosis** of the liver. Cirrhosis means that the liver is at first enlarged by the continual work that it has to do in dealing with the alcohol. Subsequently, it becomes inflamed and packed with fat. Eventually it becomes scarred and shrunken so that it can no longer function.

  A fatty liver can generally become healthy with a nutritious diet and avoiding all alcohol. Alcoholic hepatitis leads to cirrhosis in about 50 per cent of cases, but in itself is not quite as serious as cirrhosis. Cirrhosis kills about 10 per cent of people who have been problem drinkers for ten years or more.

- When you have a drink, you experience a warm glow and that signifies that many of the cells in your body are bathed in ethyl alcohol. If this happens often enough and with sufficient quantities of alcohol, then changes take place in some cells. At times, these changes can be malignant, so heavy drinkers are at a higher than average risk of **cancers** of the throat and liver.

- Some heavy drinkers suffer from **delirium tremens**. This is a dangerous state of alcohol withdrawal which causes violent tremors, hallucinations, rambling speech and hyperactivity. It usually takes place three to four days after very heavy drinking has stopped. Between 15 and 30 per cent of people with the so-called DTs die. There are several, less severe levels of withdrawal which come as soon as heavy drinking stops.

  Some heavy drinkers actually suffer alcohol-induced, epileptic-type fits.

- It is ironic that media images of drink often portray it as an *aphrodisiac* (increasing sexual desire). In fact, heavy drinking **reduces sexual function** in both men and women. **Impotence** in heavy drinkers is not uncommon.

ACTIVITY

Calorie count on popular drinks

Drink	Calories
1 pint of beer	300
1 glass of wine	80
1 whisky	90
1 vodka and orange	130

1 Compare the calorie levels above to those of fruit juices, tea, coffee, slimline tonics and bitter lemon.

2 If 10 000 extra calories can produce three pounds of fat, how much weight would you gain drinking 2.5 pints of beer each day for a fortnight?

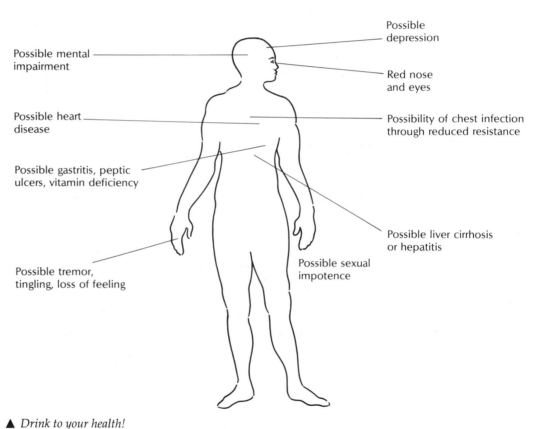

▲ *Drink to your health!*

Alcohol abuse

- Alcohol is a factor in many road deaths.
- Alcohol is a factor in many criminal offences.
- Alcohol is a factor in much family violence.

It is impossible to record the amount of misery, pain and unhappiness that heavy drinking causes in families.

Alcohol and driving

In connection with road traffic accidents, research shows that even after only two pints of beer, some people's judgement and co-ordination can be less reliable. After five pints there may be a loss of self-control, more aggression, less balance and blurred vision.

The idea of testing drivers to check alcohol levels was first introduced in 1962, but there was no maximum level fixed at that time. In 1967, the 80 mg/100 ml limit was introduced and the police had the power to stop drivers. In May 1983, a cheaper, quicker way of measuring BAC, with instant computerised print-out was initiated.

If the results are positive, then the driver is taken to the police station for further tests. In court, the lowest level reading is the one used. If the driver is found guilty then he or she may be disqualified from driving for a year and the licence is endorsed.

Female drinking patterns

During the mid 1960s and 1970s, male alcoholism doubled, but female alcoholism trebled! There are also increasing rates among women of drunk driving and arrests for drunkenness.

There has been a lot of discussion about why women are drinking more. Some suggestions are:

- That women have greater social freedom now than before.
- That women have more pressures today in that they may be expected to work inside and outside of the home.
- More women do work and, therefore, have more financial independence.
- It is now more socially acceptable for women to drink.
- Drinks favoured by women, such as gin, sherry and liqueurs, have actually gone down in price in real terms.

Whatever the reason, the effects are serious. Women can damage their livers by drinking smaller amounts and over a shorter period of time than their male counterparts. Similarly, women are more at risk from brain damage, certain cancers and ulcers. They become physically dependent on alcohol more quickly than men, so they show withdrawal symptoms earlier.

During pregnancy, drinking is especially dangerous as it can damage the foetus.

ACTIVITY

Quiz – How much do you know about alcohol?
Comment on the following statements – are they true or false? Give reasons for your decision.

1 Alcohol warms you up on a cold day.

2 Alcohol makes you sleep well.

3 Alcohol causes as much damage in society as heroin.

4 Alcohol provides important dietary requirements.

5 Alcohol is OK taken with mild tranquillisers.

6 The effects of alcohol are temporary.

7 Women get drunk more easily than men.

8 Alcohol is a stimulant.

9 Only the liver can remove alcohol from the bloodstream.

10 The best advice to pregnant women is to abstain from alcohol completely.

11 It takes about four hours for your body to eliminate two pints of beer.

12 Drinking spirits is more dangerous than drinking beer.

ACTIVITY

Controlling alcohol consumption
Make a list of the reasons why you think people drink. Think about why you drink yourself. Then look at the list of reasons below and comment on them in the light of what you have read in this chapter.

- It helps me relax.
- It helps me to feel confident.
- It helps me pull myself together.
- It helps me sleep.
- I like to be sociable.
- I enjoy the taste.
- I find it refreshing.
- I drink out of habit.
- I drink to forget my worries.
- I drink when I am under pressure at work.

ACTIVITY

Keeping a drink diary
If you are worried about how much you drink or even how much you spend on drink, a useful monitoring exercise is to keep a drink diary.

Record your alcohol consumption every day for about 12 weeks. It may help to use the headings below so that you can see if any particular patterns emerge.

Date	Time	Hours spent	Place	Money spent	Units consumed	Other activities	With whom	Consequences/ how you felt
Sun 4/11/90	12.30–1.30 p.m.	1.5	'Hammer & Pincers' pub		2.5	Darts	George and Alex	Quite relaxed; good chat about football
5/11/90	7 p.m.–10.30 p.m.	3.5	West End		10	None	Nobody	Had awful day at work; drank to console myself; felt very rough Tues a.m.
9/11/90	8 p.m.	1.5	'Hammer & Pincers' pub		2	Cards	George and Alex	Good – enjoyed myself.

Once you have kept your diary ask yourself:

1 Did you drink more than you intended to in each case?

2 Do you sometimes regret how much you drank the day before?

3 Does your drinking ever cause trouble?

Very heavy drinkers are sometimes encouraged to draw up 'troublesome' and 'trouble-free' drink diaries. Obviously, factors like who you are drinking with, how much money and time you spend and whether drinking is the sole activity, all affect consumption levels. Below is a list of steps which you may consider if you are trying to reduce your alcohol intake or if you are working with people who are trying to cut down.

How to cut down

- Tell people you are cutting down, but be careful as some may use this as provocation and aim to make you drink.
- Start drinking later than you do at present.
- Take smaller sips.
- Put your glass down between sips.
- Occupy yourself, either with an activity or by conversation.
- Do not take spirits and lager or beer together; you take in alcohol much faster that way.
- Dilute spirits with water or a mixer.
- Eat a meal before you drink.
- Learn to refuse drinks.
- Know *exactly* how much you have drunk.
- Have some 'rest days' when you do not drink at all.
- Learn to relax without drinking – see the section on Stress in this chapter.

Obviously, if people have serious drink problems then professional help must be sought. People may need help for underlying problems like bereavement, marital strains or pressures from work. Some psychiatric hospitals run group therapy sessions at alcohol treatment units. In severe cases, people may need to be admitted to hospital for de-toxification or 'drying out'. This does not cure alcoholism, but helps to arrest the physical damage incurred by it.

DRUGS

The definition of illegal drugs

Drug misuse means those forms of drug-taking which meet with social disapproval. This includes possession, for non-medical use, of illegal drugs under the Misuse of Drugs Act 1972. Cannabis, LSD, opiates, amphetamines and solvents are all illegal drugs.

Numbers of young people involved with drugs

A *New Society Survey*, carried out in 1986, found that 17 per cent of secondary school pupils used cannabis; 6 per cent solvents and 2 per cent heroin. Asian pupils registered the lowest number for the question asking whether they had ever tried drugs. Some schools were particularly high, for example one boys' school in Glasgow where 20 per cent of pupils were involved with solvent misuse.

Studies indicate that problematic drug-taking is worse in the cities and in areas of high unemployment and social deprivation. Official statistics demonstrate an overall increase in the number of drug addicts. If drug addicts inject they run a strong risk of contracting AIDS (Acquired Immune Deficiency Syndrome).

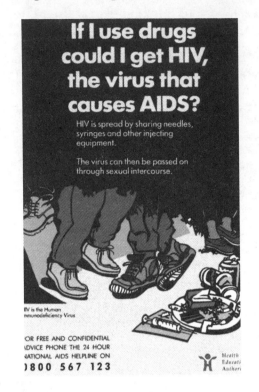

Why people misuse drugs

People take illegal drugs for all sorts of reasons from curiosity to searching for some form of escape. Studies indicate four main reasons why people take drugs:

- a mixture of curiosity and pleasure seeking;
- encouragement from peers;
- to relieve stress or solve problems, but mostly as a gesture of rebellion rather than deep anxiety;
- availability – if drugs are around at a party or concert there is often pressure to take them.

Help available for drug users

The majority of drug users do not come into contact with health service personnel unless the toxic effects of the drugs do evident damage or because a relative is worried about them.

People who work with drug users have found that multi-disciplinary teams obtain the most effective results. This means drawing staff from health, probation, social services and voluntary organisations together to work in teams. They can then work with the individual as a total person discussing and co-ordinating their broad approach. It is in this way that the psychological, social, emotional and economic needs of the user are taken into account.

Table 5.2 shows some common illegal drugs, how they are used and the effects they have both short- and long-term.

Drug	Nicknames	Use	Effect
Cannabis	Dope, Pot, Blow, Weed, Smoke, Tea, Puff.	Smoked in the form of 'joints' (hand-rolled cigarettes).	Loss of sense of time, relaxes and also heightens appreciation of music and colour.
LSD (Lysergic Acid Diethylamide)	Acid, flash, sugar, paper mushrooms.	Tablet form or impregnated onto sheets of paper. Sometimes taken on a sugar cube or set in gelatine.	Main damage is psychological.
Cocaine	Coke, Charlie Girl, Lady, Toot, Happy, Dust, Candy.	Can be mixed with flour, baking powder and water, and even cooked. Can also be smoked.	Strong psychological dependence, nausea, restlessness and insomnia.
Barbiturates	Barbs, Goof balls.	Tablet form.	Psychological dependence; sudden withdrawal can be fatal.
Heroin	Junk, Horse, Dragon, Henry.	Injected or smoked.	Range of physical effects. Higher doses can produce sedation, stupor and coma.
Amphetamines	Speed, Whizz, Wake-ups.	Tablet form or injected.	Stimulates the central nervous system. Long-term use can affect the heart.

Table 5.2 *Illegal drug uses and effects*

Everyday drugs

The drugs described above are illegal and potentially very dangerous. It is interesting to note, however, that tea, coffee and cocoa all contain active chemicals, caffeine, theophylline and theobrimine, which are absorbed into the bloodstream. The structure of these chemicals is similar to that of adrenaline, the body's own stimulant.

Food or drink	Amount of caffeine it contains
1 cup of instant coffee	90 mgs of caffeine
1 cup of filter coffee	200 mgs of caffeine
1 cup of tea (depending on how long you allow it to brew)	40–70 mgs of caffeine
1 can of coca-cola	40 mgs of caffeine
1 150 gm bar of plain chocolate	100 mgs of caffeine
1 150 gm bar of milk chocolate	30 mgs of caffeine

Table 5.3 *Amounts of caffeine in different food and drink*

People who drink more than two cups of coffee or four cups of tea per day will have levels of chemicals in their bloodstream which will keep their 'rate of arousal' at a higher than normal level. Maintaining an artificially high level of arousal will reduce your ability to cope with any additional stress, and will keep your body and mind in perpetual tension. When tea and coffee are reduced you may well feel lethargic and slow for a few days. You may even develop a 'coffee withdrawal' headache. Table 5.3 shows a list of caffeine indicators. The recommended adult intake of coffee is two cups per day and for tea, four cups. Have you tried herbal teas, many of which contain none of the active chemicals mentioned above?

Solvents

Several hundred substances can be used for solvent abuse; glue, paint, petrol and lighter fuel are just a few. The solvent vapours act as a depressant and hallucinations can be experienced when solvents are inhaled.

Accidental death or injury can happen because the 'sniffer' (solvent user) is 'drunk', especially if they are sniffing in an unsafe environment, such as on a roof or near a canal bank. Sniffing to the point of becoming unconscious risks death through choking on vomit. Very long-term use might cause brain damage. The after-effects of poor concentration, fatigue and forgetfulness can become habitual and affect whole lifestyles and opportunities.

It is an offence for shopkeepers to sell potentially dangerous solvents to people under 18 years of age.

ACTIVITY

1 Find out what help is available within your own community for people involved with drugs.

2 Organise a display warning people of the dangers of illegal drug taking. You could:
   a) Check out suitable places to mount the display, for example in the college reception area or library.
   b) Contact your Local Health Promotion Authority for posters and pamphlets.
   c) Research your own information from as many sources as you can, for example, magazines, books, journals and videos, and use the computer to word-process and present them well.
   d) Capitalise on the artistic talent within the group. There is bound to be some eye-catching methods of presentation. Make sure all work is correct, neat, straight and well mounted.

AIDS

AIDS stands for Acquired Immune Deficiency Syndrome:

- **Acquired** – it is caught from someone or something;
- **Immune Deficiency** – you have an immune deficiency when your body cannot defend itself against certain illnesses;
- **Syndrome** – the particular pattern of illnesses you can get as a result.

AIDS is a disease which results from contracting HIV (Human Immune Deficiency Virus).

Numbers of victims

By the end of 1991, AIDS had resulted in over 3 391 deaths in Britain since the first case was recorded in 1981. 5 451 cases of AIDS were recorded at the end of 1991 and over 950 of these are or were heterosexual men and women. The disturbing aspect of AIDS, however, is that the number of AIDS cases is doubling every 10 months and at least 30 000 people are thought to be virus carriers (i.e. potential AIDS victims). Experts fear that there may be an epidemic; AIDS could be the greatest public health problem of the century.

Groups at risk

The main groups are:

- sexual partners of AIDS sufferers or virus carriers;
- homosexuals and bi-sexuals;
- drug addicts;
- sufferers of a blood disorder called *haemophilia*;
- babies born to AIDS sufferers or virus carriers;
- prostitutes (both male and female).

However, all sexually-active people are at risk if they have several partners and do not protect themselves.

How the virus is spread

The virus is found in its most concentrated form in the blood and sperm and so any form of sex that involves penetration into the body can spread the disease. Thus all types of *unprotected intercourse*, that is intercourse without using condoms, can spread the virus. The risk can be reduced but not eliminated if condoms are used.

Needles and syringes shared by drug addicts can cause blood infection. This means that the virus can be passed from one addict to another via the same needle or syringe.

Some haemophiliacs who suffer from a blood-clotting disorder have been infected by contaminated doses of a blood product called *Factor B* which is now heat-treated to destroy the virus. A few people have been infected through ordinary blood transfusions.

People can actually be 'carriers' of the virus (they are called *HIV positive*), without showing signs of the AIDS condition itself. They can knowingly or unknowingly infect other people. The carriers can be healthy for years.

The effects of AIDS

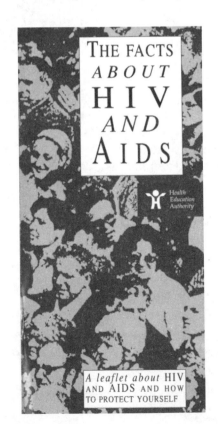

Those who demonstrate signs of the AIDS condition may be ill for nine months to six years. About 50 per cent die within a year of diagnosis.

Once a diagnosis of AIDS is made it obviously has many far-reaching implications, practically, socially and medically, for the individual. First, AIDS sufferers may be refused insurance and mortgages. Secondly, other people may feel that they may also contract the virus and be uncertain about relating to the sufferer. Finally, there is no cure at present for the disease.

Help available

GU (Genito Urinary) clinics:

- can give general advice about AIDS;
- can give the HIV antibody test (the test that shows if you are HIV positive and so have the virus that could develop into AIDS);
- offer special advice and counselling from people who have the virus or AIDS itself.

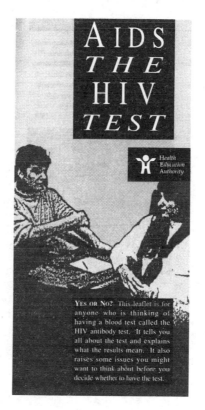

The advice and treatment is free and confidential. You do not need a letter from your doctor. At some clinics you can just turn up but it is best to phone first to check. The number will be in the telephone directory. If you have difficulty, then phone your nearest main hospital.

The Terence Higgins Trust, based in London:

- offers help and counselling to people with the virus or AIDS itself, and their friends or relatives;
- gives detailed information on what is 'safe sex' and what is 'risky sex';
- gives advice and information to people thinking about having the HIV antibody test. Your own doctor can advise and arrange for you to have the test.

Smoking Survey

Aims

1 To produce a survey on smoking in your college to find out the proportion of students who smoke and what is the general attitude to smoking.

2 To develop common skills, specifically with regard to:
   - research techniques;
   - designing questions;
   - approaching people;
   - analysing data;
   - evaluating data;
   - writing and presenting information.

Preparation

1 Use your own college as a base but decide which section of people using the college you are going to survey, for example, staff, full-time students, part-time students or support staff.

2 Think carefully about your choice of sample. Remember you will have to approach these people with questionnaires. How feasible is it to question ancillary or support staff, bearing in mind that they may work irregular hours?

3 Once you have decided on your sample, make a list of the limiting factors concerning that group of people. For example, if you choose full-time students you will note that the vast majority of them will be young. Furthermore, you are dealing with a particular group who want to study. Your findings may be different for young people who are in work.

4 In small groups, draft out lists of questions relating to the sort of information you want to gain from the survey. You will need some basic information, such as age and gender, but it may also be interesting to consider issues like how many people want the college to be absolutely smoke-free.

5 The next stage is to refine your questions so that they are clear. You might try them out amongst yourselves. You should consider how open or closed the questions are.

6 Design the questionnaire; you may be able to use your information technology skills here.

7 Plan a strategy to carry out the questionnaire process with your sample using the whole group. Then set deadlines for completing the survey.

8 Organise groups to analyse your completed questionnaires. Different groups could analyse different sections or questions of the survey. Set a deadline for analysis of the information gained.

9 Organise a total group session to feed back and co-ordinate findings.

10 Individuals should then write up a conclusion to the survey.

11 Evaluate the whole exercise by listing the aspects of the survey which went well and the reasons for this. Also record the difficulties you came across.

6 Human growth and development

AIMS

▶ To gain a basic knowledge of human growth and development.

▶ To use this knowledge in understanding the needs of clients at various ages and stages of development.

INTRODUCTION

Where does human growth and development begin? Most of us believe that human life actually begins at the moment of conception. However, it is helpful to begin by looking at the development of relationships between men and women before they consider conceiving a child.

The pattern of development towards becoming a 'couple' will tend to follow a certain path. First, there is the single-sex group within which social activities occur; later mixed groups evolve. Girls will tend to limit themselves to one or two close friends. Later they start to concern themselves with boys and the approval of boys becomes more important than acceptance by their female peers. Then mixed groups of couples and their friends begin to develop. Later peer groups will tend to break up and couples dominate the social scene. Couples may develop an interest in sexual relationships, hopefully within a framework of respect and caring.

ACTIVITY

1 What do you think it means to be a 'couple'? Discuss this with your student colleagues.

2 Which qualities do you think you will look for when choosing a partner?

3 Complete the quiz below, writing your responses on a piece of paper. Discuss the responses with other students and with your tutor.

Quiz

Qualities	Score									
	1	2	3	4	5	6	7	8	9	10
Good wage earner										
Good looking										
Good sense of humour										
Handyman/woman										
Intelligent										
Good with children										
Likes a good social life										
Rich										
Hardworking										
Manages money well										

Give a score out of ten showing the importance you attach to each quality.

REPRODUCTION

It is important to know the correct names for the various parts of the male and female reproductive organs and to understand their functions. This information will be relevant when you discuss caring skills and health education.

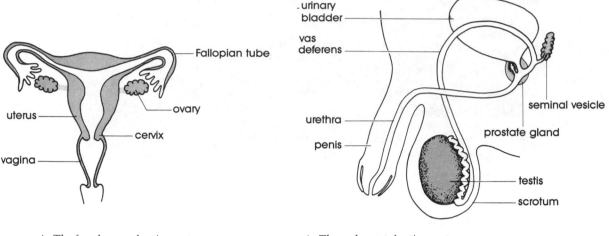

▲ *The female reproductive system*

▲ *The male reproductive system*

Sexual intercourse – what happens?

The sexual act should be carried out with love and affection. It should be an experience that can be enjoyed by both partners.

The following stages will usually occur:

- mutual attraction;
- kissing, cuddling and touching;

For the woman –
- the vagina becomes moist;
- the clitoris becomes firm;
- a lubricating fluid is produced;

For the man –
- the penis becomes erect;
- the penis enters the vagina;

- the couple become more sexually aroused as a result of the frictional movements between penis and vagina/clitoris;
- climax/orgasm (men experience one orgasm when sperm is ejaculated, women may experience more than one).

Mutual pleasure and consideration for each other will ensure that both partners find sexual intercourse a satisfying experience.

Sperm cells are produced in a man's testes. They are stored in special sperm ducts and are released in a liquid called *seminal fluid*. They are among the smallest cells in the body, but they have a head, a middle piece and a tail. The *nucleus* (the main or central part), which contains only one set of chromosomes, is in the head. Sperm move by lashing their tails and energy for this action is supplied from the middle part of the cell.

Egg cells are produced in a woman's ovaries. Each month one (usually but sometimes several) becomes ripe and is released from the ovaries into a nearby fallopian tube where tiny hairs help the *ovum* (the egg cell) drift down towards the *uterus* (womb). The ovum is in a state of ripeness for about two days. If it does not meet a sperm cell during this time it dies. Like the nucleus of the sperm cell the ovum contains only one set of chromosomes.

Fertilisation of the ovum (egg cell)

During sexual intercourse a small amount of fluid containing millions of sperm cells is expelled through the man's penis and deposited in the woman's vagina, just below the uterus. The sperm make their way to the ovum which is present in the fallopian tube. Assisted by movements of the vagina and uterus some of the sperm manage to swim into the uterus. Only the very strongest sperm pass through the uterus into the fallopian tubes. Finally, a few hundred sperm approach the ovum although only one sperm cell will be successful in fertilising the ovum.

The stages in fertilisation

- The sperm cells release digestive enzymes to help penetrate the ovum's jelly coating.
- A few sperm cells pass straight through the jelly coating and reach the ovum.
- One sperm cell penetrates the membrane surrounding the ovum. Other sperm are prevented from entering by changes in the membrane and protective jelly-like coating.
- The nucleus of the sperm cell moves towards the nucleus of the ovum and the two nuclei merge into one.
- The fertilised ovum moves from the fallopian tube and implants itself in the uterus.

What problems may people experience?

Couples may encounter a variety of problems in sexual relationships including premature ejaculation, impotence, frigidity and loss of interest in sex. Discussion of any problems between partners is very important and help and advice are available from family planning clinics and doctors.

ACTIVITY

Some people argue that sexual intercourse is only for the purpose of producing children. What do you think?

Contraception

Contraception means 'against conceiving', that is the measures men and women can take to prevent pregnancy. It is an important topic, as knowing the methods available means that sensible choices can be made.

ACTIVITY

1 Find out all you can about the methods of contraception which are currently available.

2 Write up your findings, giving a rating to the effectiveness of the various methods.

3 In your local area, find out what facilities are available for young people to obtain contraceptive advice.

4 Find out and report on any new methods of contraception which are being developed.

Pre-conceptual care

Pre-conceptual care can seriously affect the subsequent growth and development of human beings. In the period of time between a couple deciding that they would like a baby and the time of conception (the pre-conceptual period) much can be done to ensure the baby's good health and sound future development. It is mainly the mother who should look after herself by eating well, taking regular exercise and avoiding harmful substances, such as alcohol, tobacco and drugs.

ACTIVITY

Find out if there is a clinic in your local community where advice is available on pre-conceptual care.

Pregnancy

Doctors and midwives time pregnancy from the first day of a woman's last period, *not* from conception. Therefore, what is called four weeks pregnant is actually approximately two weeks after conception. Using this method of timing, pregnancy lasts for 40 weeks. This is an average time; some pregnancies are shorter and some longer.

What are the signs of pregnancy?
Usually the first sign of pregnancy is a missed monthly period. Other signs include:

- feeling or being sick;
- breast tenderness;
- needing to pass urine more frequently;
- constipation;
- increased vaginal discharge which should be colourless and odourless;
- feeling tired;
- a metallic taste in the mouth;
- going off certain foods;
- craving for certain foods.

Emotional changes

It is generally argued that pregnant women are very happy, they appear to bloom and eagerly anticipate the birth. In fact women experience a variety of emotions during their pregnancies, some positive and others negative. Here are some feelings which have been expressed by pregnant women:

- 'I'm fine. I feel really happy, but I get so tired.'
- 'I get so depressed being in the house all the time on my own. I feel like a recluse.'
- 'I get upset more quickly. The slightest little mishap and I'm upset.'
- 'I feel contented and happy within myself, happy with the world.'
- 'I think I have more extremes of emotion. I get more easily upset about things and can easily get very happy about things.'
- 'I've enjoyed it. I've enjoyed the newness of it. I've enjoyed thinking about the baby. The only thing I haven't really enjoyed is getting so big.'
- 'I worry about the birth, what I've got to go through. People tell you different things so you don't know what to think.'

A first baby is bound to bring about some quite big changes in a couple's relationship.

Here are some thoughts which have been expressed by couples:

- 'You've got a bond between you. It's something that belongs to both of you.'
- 'Sometimes it draws us together and other times it sets us apart. When we first found about the baby we were on edge. We snapped at each other rather a lot. Then it improved. We really wanted each other and were looking forward to the baby coming. It's up and down.'
- 'It can be difficult in early pregnancy for fathers to believe the baby is actually there. Once they can actually feel the baby moving they begin to look forward to parenthood. Fathers have an important role in providing emotional support for the mother.'

In some ways pregnancy can be a very private thing, but of course the whole family will be affected. Older children need to be introduced to the idea of a new brother or sister over a period of time.

Not every pregnant mother has the help and support of a partner. Single or unsupported mothers, whilst sharing the same physical and emotional changes, will experience extra responsibilities because they are alone.

ACTIVITY

Think of some of the difficulties which may be experienced by a single parent. Suggest ways in which the difficulties may be overcome. You could work in pairs and prepare a short summary.

Ante-natal care

Ante-natal care is preventive medicine concerned with detecting potential problems in the mother and the unborn baby. Ante-natal care consists of:

- regular medical check-ups;
- carrying out special tests where these may be necessary to monitor progress, for example, amniocentesis and ultra-sound scanning;
- making a birth plan;
- instruction on the various aspects of child care.

How does the baby develop?

In the very early weeks, the developing baby is called an *embryo*. From about eight weeks onwards it is called a *foetus*, meaning 'young one'.

ACTIVITY

1 Find out the timing of the various stages of development of the foetus in the uterus.

2 Produce a chart or graph which will show the approximate times when the following milestones in development will occur:
- fertilisation;
- implantation;
- head and eyes can be recognised;
- placenta has formed;
- recognisably human;
- heartbeat can be heard through a stethoscope;
- mother can feel limb movements in the womb;
- foetus weighs about 1 kilogram;
- survival possible if foetus is separated from the mother;
- pregnancy at full-term.

At the end of the pregnancy the baby is usually in the head-down position ready for the birth.

THE NEWBORN

When a baby is born, one of the first questions a mother may well ask is 'Is my baby normal?' In order to check that all is well, a number of tests are carried out on the baby.

- The airway, palate and colour are examined.
- A test, called the *apgar score*, is used to check the baby's responses, such as pulse and respiration. It is carried out at certain time intervals.
- The hips are checked in case there is any evidence of dislocation.
- The genitalia are examined.
- The heart is checked with a stethoscope.
- Head size, birth weight and length are recorded.
- Skin colour is observed. Sometimes new babies may be jaundiced (especially if they are premature) and appear yellow. This is due to an immature liver and the condition is usually temporary.

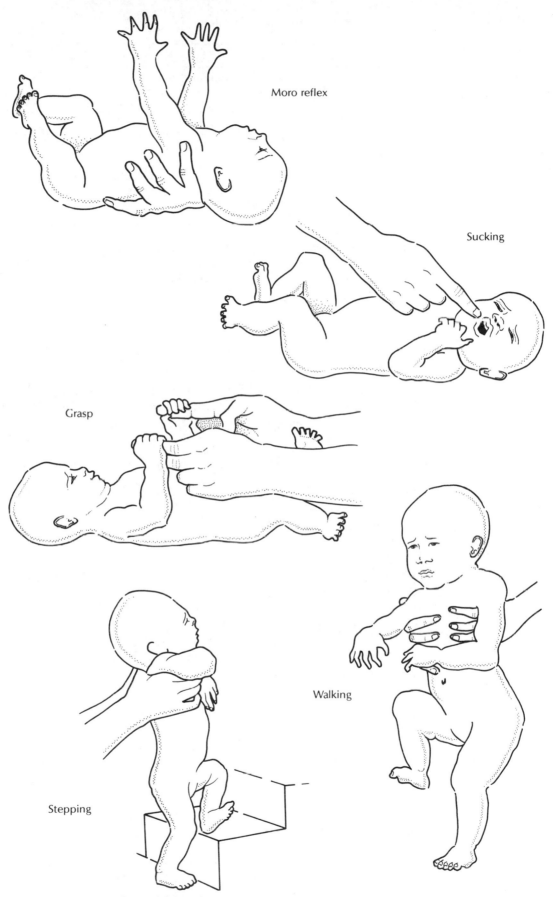

Moro reflex

Sucking

Grasp

Walking

Stepping

▲ *Figure 6.1 Reflexes of the newborn*

Average weight	3.5 kilograms
Average length	50 cm
Head size	30–50 cm
Fontanelles	Soft areas at the front and back of head
Lanugo	Downy hair covering the body
Vernix	White, protective grease covering the skin
Umbilicus	Remains of the umbilical cord
Moulding of head	Shaping which may occur during delivery

At birth, a baby is a very helpless creature. Compared with other animals the human infant is the most helpless and its growth is very slow. The new baby cries to attract mother's attention and after a few weeks will smile and show pleasure when mother or father appears.

Reflexes

When a baby is born certain primitive reflexes are present. Some reflexes are protective and others reflect behaviour which can only have been present at an earlier stage of human evolution. Reflexes tend to disappear by the time the baby is three months old, an age when the baby begins to consciously make movements on his or her own.

The following reflexes are normally present at birth (see Figure 6.1):

- the sucking reflex;
- the swallowing reflex;
- the rooting reflex – if one side of a baby's cheek or mouth is gently touched, the head will turn in the direction of the touch;
- the grasping reflex – the fist clenches if an object is placed in the palm;
- the Moro reflex – in response to being startled, arms and legs are flung out and then drawn inwards;
- the stepping reflex – if the front of a leg is brought into contact with the edge of a table a baby will raise a leg to 'step' up;
- the walking reflex – if a baby is held upright with the soles of his or her feet on a flat surface and is then moved forward, he or she will respond by making 'walking' steps.

ACTIVITY

Arrange to interview a mother who has a baby under the age of three months and ask for her to demonstrate the grasping or sucking reflexes with her baby.

CHILD DEVELOPMENT

Knowing what the average baby or child can reasonably be expected to do helps the family and carers to recognise potential problems and if appropriate to plan suitable exercises and activities to correct these.

The process of development begins at conception. The sequence of development is normally the same for all children, but the *rate* of development will vary from child to child. Parts of the body near the brain develop first, for example, active use of the mouth, the eyes and hearing come before sitting, walking and use of fingers.

Those who study human development have offered a number of ways to group functions. One popular way is to study development under the general headings of:

- **physical** – meaning the development of the body, balance and control of body movements;
- **intellectual** – the development of thinking, recognition, reasoning, knowing and understanding;
- **emotional** – the development of feelings, including excitement, love, happiness, anger, contentment, pride, jealousy, shyness and frustration;
- **social** – including personal care and play, learning to interact in groups and sharing.

It is important to make a distinction between 'growth' and 'development'. When we refer to *growth* we mean an increase in actual size; when we discuss *development* we mean an increase in complexity. For example, becoming taller is an obvious increase in size. However, the ability to reach for objects or transfer them from hand to hand shows a development of complex skills.

When looking at human development we must also consider the fulfilment of certain basic needs which are both *physical* and *psychological*.

ACTIVITY

Discuss within your group and then make a list of the things you consider to be basic human needs.

Does your list look something like this?

Physical needs	*Psychological needs*
• Shelter	• Affection
• Protection	• Continuous individual care
• Fresh air and sunlight	• Security
• Activity and rest	• Personal identity
• Prevention of illness or injury	• Dignity and self-respect
• Training in life skills	• Opportunity to learn from experience.

From birth to three years

This age group are generally referred to as infants in the first year and toddlers in the second and third years of life. We will consider the physical, intellectual, emotional and social aspects of development mentioned earlier, applied to this group.

One way to begin to explain human development from birth to three years is to study Table 6.1.

Age	Physical development	Intellectual development	Emotional development	Social development
1 month	Holds head erect for a few seconds. Eyes follow a moving light.	Interested in sounds.	Cries in response to pain, hunger and thirst.	May sleep up to 20 hours in a 24-hour period. Stops crying when picked up and spoken to.
3 months	Eyes follow a person moving. Kicks vigorously.	Recognises carer's face. Shows excitement. Listens, smiles, holds rattle.	Enjoys being cuddled and played with. Misses carer and cries for him/her to return.	Responds happily to carer. Becomes excited at prospect of a feed or bath.
6 months	Able to lift head and chest up supported by wrists. Turns to a person who is speaking.	Responds to speech. Vocalises. Uses eyes a lot. Holds toys. Explores using hands. Listens to sound.	Can be anxious in presence of strangers. Can show anger and frustration. Shows a clear preference for mother's company.	Puts everything in mouth. Plays with hands and feet. Tries to hold bottle when feeding.
9 months	Stands when supported. May crawl. Gazes at self in mirror. Tries to hold drinking cup. Sits without support.	Tries to talk, babbling. May say 'Mama' and 'Dada'. Shouts for attention. Understands 'No'.	Can recognise individuals – mother, father, siblings. Still anxious about strangers. Sometimes irritable if routine is altered.	Plays 'Peek a boo'. Imitates hand clapping. Puts hands round cup when feeding.
12 months	Pulls self up to standing position. Uses pincer grip. Feeds self using fingers. May walk without assistance.	Knows own name. Obeys simple instructions. Says about three words.	Shows affection. Gives kisses and cuddles. Likes to see familiar faces but less worried by strangers.	Drinks from a cup without assistance. Holds a spoon but cannot feed him/herself. Plays 'Pat-a-Cake'. Quickly finds hidden toys.
1.5 years	Walks well, feet apart. Runs carefully. Pushes and pulls large toys. Walks upstairs. Creeps backwards downstairs	Uses 6–20 recognisable words. Repeats last word of short sentences. Enjoys and tries to join in with nursery rhymes. Picks up named toys. Enjoying looking at simple picture books. Builds a tower of 3–4 bricks. Scribbles and makes dots. Preference for right or left hand shown.	Affectionate, but may still be reserved with strangers. Likes to see familiar faces.	Able to hold spoon and to get food into mouth. Holds drinking cup and hands it back when finished. Can take off shoes and socks. Bowel control may have been achieved. Remembers where objects belong.
2 years	Runs on whole foot. Squats steadily. Climbs on furniture. Throws a small ball. Sits on a small tricycle and moves vehicle with feet.	Uses 50 or more recognisable words; understands many more words; put two or three words together to form simple sentences. Refers to self by name. Asks names of objects and people. Scribbles in circles. Can build a tower of six or seven cubes. Hand preference is obvious.	Can display negative behaviour and resistance. May have temper tantrums if thwarted. Plays contentedly beside other children but not with them. Constantly demands mother's attention.	Asks for food and drink. Spoon feeds without spilling. Puts on shoes.

Table 6.1 *Continued*

2.5 years	All locomotive skills now improving. Runs and climbs. Able to jump from a low step with feet together. Kicks a large ball.	May use 200 or more words. Knows full name. Continually asking questions, likes stories and recognises details in picture books. Recognises self in photographs. Builds a tower of seven or more cubes.	Usually active and restless. Emotionally still very dependent on adults. Tends not to want to share playthings.	Eats skilfully with a spoon and may sometimes use a fork. Active and restless. Often dry through the day.
3 years	Sits with feet crossed at ankles. Walks upstairs using alternating feet.	Able to state full name, sex and sometimes age. Carries on simple conversations and constantly questioning. Demands favourite story over and over again. Can count to 10 by rote. Can thread wooden beads on string. Can copy a circle and a cross. Names colours. Cuts with scissors. Paints with a large brush.	Becomes less prone to temper tantrums. Affectionate and confiding, showing affection for younger siblings. Begins to understand sharing.	Eats with a fork and spoon. May be dry through the night.

Table 6.1 *Child's development – birth to three years*

ACTIVITY

Read the list of actions printed below.

1 Arrange to interview a parent of a child under the age of four years to find out when the child was first observed carrying out the actions indicated in the list below.

2 Take your own chart displaying:
   a) the actions;
   b) the average age when the actions would be accomplished;
   c) the age when the child was observed carrying out the actions.

List of actions

- Eyes followed a moving light
- Smiled
- Reached for a toy
- Slept through the night
- Sat without support
- Crawled
- Stood up without support
- Walked without assistance
- Threw a small ball
- Spoke first word
- Put two or three words together
- Used a spoon and fork
- Dry during the day
- Dry during the night
- Achieved bowel control
- Built a tower of three bricks
- Drew a circle
- Showed preference for right or left hand
- Drank from a cup without assistance
- Began to understand sharing.

Pre-school children

Children between the ages of three and five are termed *pre-school children*. They are increasingly active and communicative. During your work placement you will probably experience looking after children of this age group. Some of the abilities you can expect to observe may be grouped under the headings of:

- physical development
- intellectual development
- emotional development
- social development.

Physical development

Between the ages of three and five years the child develops and perfects many of the physical skills which have been acquired since birth. Accomplishments include running, climbing, riding a tricycle, sitting cross-legged, moving in time with music and playing ball games.

Intellectual development

During this period, a child will begin to speak grammatically, recount recent events accurately, enjoy jokes and be able to state their name, address, age and usually birthday.

The child will be gaining control in writing and drawing. A recognisable person may be drawn, also a house which has doors, windows and a roof. Pictures are coloured neatly and four or more primary colours can be named.

Emotional development

Children of this age need the companionship of other children. They are gradually becoming more independent. They will comfort playmates who are upset, will choose their own friends and are beginning to understand the rules of fair play.

Social development

By the age of five a child is able to use a knife, fork and spoon. They can dress and undress themselves, although they may have some difficulty with fastenings. They indulge in make-believe play and in general are more sensible. They relate clock time to daily programmes of events.

The carers

At birth, the newborn infant is assessed by the paediatrician and the midwife will monitor the baby's progress for the first ten days. Throughout the first year, the infant is supported by the health visitor and/or the doctor. Assessments continue at less frequent intervals until the age of five years.

Five to ten years of age

At about five years of age the child will usually start to attend school. What do you expect from a child of this age? We have discussed the physical, intellectual, emotional and social changes which have taken place between birth and five years in some detail. For ages five to ten a more general outline will be given. Use this as a framework for making your own placement observations.

Physical appearance

The five-year-old appears taller and slimmer than the toddler and features have a more adult look. Movements are well co-ordinated. Growth rate will now be steady until the age of puberty.

Intellect

The child begins to develop a greater capacity for directed thinking. During your work-experience placements some of you will be able to observe at first-hand how children learn the range of activities designed by teachers to stimulate children to acquire knowledge and skills.

Emotions

If a child has not been separated from a parent before entering school he or she may experience problems of adjustment. Carers working or helping with children of this age should be sensitive to this situation. Try thinking back to your own first day at school and your feelings at that time. Discuss with your parents what your reactions were at that period.

Relationships

At birth, the child begins to relate first to mother and then to father, brothers, sisters and other relations. This range of contacts will be extended when school starts. In school, the teacher may inherit the role of the parents in the child's eyes, but it is not possible for the teacher to give undivided attention to every child. Sometimes a child who is used to a lot of individual attention from the mother or father may find this difficult to adjust to at first.

ACTIVITY

Starting school for the first time may prove to be a difficult experience for a four- or five-year-old child.

After questioning teachers, care assistants, parents and your friends, produce an advice sheet which would help parents to prepare their child for starting school.

The life of a child in this age group revolves around the family, school and the community. Independence is increasing and variations in ability levels become more obvious.

Between the ages of seven and ten girls tend to develop more rapidly than boys, both physically and intellectually. Boys and girls in this age group tend not to play together. During your work placement you may have noticed this. Boys will tend to play football and other games in groups while girls have their own activities and games. Physical growth continues but not as rapidly as at earlier stages. Physical skill increases and boys will indulge in a lot of rough-and-tumble.

By the time a child is nine, special friendships will have been developed. However, nine-year-olds may be very critical of each other and will often exclude individuals from games. By the age of ten childhood is nearing completion and puberty is beginning. The skills of the ten-year-old bring together all that has been experienced and learned in childhood.

ADOLESCENCE

Adolescence is the name usually given to the period of life between the age of ten and 18, the onset of puberty to adult life. It is a time of social and biological change. In some cultures, adolescence is an abrupt division between childhood and adult life and may be marked by a specific initiation ceremony. In Britain today, the tendency is to prolong adolescence, whereas in Victorian times children were sent to work at an early age, thereby denying them the opportunity to gain experience through adolescence.

During these years an adolescent may become a parent, leave home, drive a car, start work, smoke, drink and vote.

Puberty

Puberty means 'age of manhood'. Physical changes occur because of increased production of hormones; oestrogen in girls and testosterone in boys.

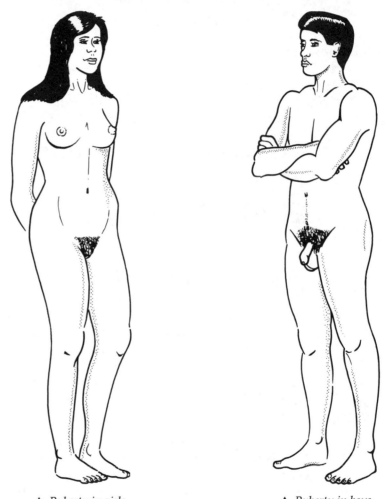

▲ *Puberty in girls*   ▲ *Puberty in boys*

Puberty in girls

Changes in girls tend to start at ten to 12 years of age, sometimes even earlier. These include:

- a growth spurt;
- breast development;
- appearance of pubic and armpit hair;

- broadening of the hips;
- a redistribution of fat;
- menstruation.

Puberty in boys

In boys, the changes associated with puberty usually start at 12 to 14 years of age: These include:

- a growth spurt;
- facial hair;
- deepening of the voice;
- enlargement of the penis, scrotum and testes;
- appearance of pubic, chest and armpit hair;
- the limbs lengthen and shoulders become more broad;
- an ability to ejaculate.

What adolescents have to say about adolescence

- 'My parents don't like my clothes, hair or friends.'
- 'I have these awful mood changes.'
- 'I feel so shy and embarrassed.'
- 'I think I look a mess.'
- 'I don't think that other people really like me.'
- 'I'm a bit worried about my sexuality. Should I be considering a sexual relationship?'
- 'I can't concentrate on my school or college work.'
- 'I wonder if my parents prefer my brother and sister to me.'
- 'I'm too fat/thin.'
- 'I've got spots.'
- 'I've got a crush on another boy/girl.'
- 'Should I try drinking, smoking or drugs?'
- 'I wish I had more independence.'

ACTIVITY

1 Find out as much as you can about the problems associated with adolescence.

2 Prepare a 'Problem Page' which might appear in a teenage magazine by writing a selection of letters asking advice on a range of adolescent issues.

3 From your reading and research give concise answers to the letters.

The rights and responsibilities of an adolescent

- Age 10 years – age of criminal responsibility.
- Age 12 years – can purchase a pet.
- Age 14 years – can go unaccompanied to see a film classified PG (Parental Guidance); can own an airgun; can enter a bar accompanied by an adult but not allowed alcoholic drinks.
- Age 16 years – can buy cigarettes; can give own consent for medical treatment; contraceptive help is available to girls without parental consent.
- Age 17 years – can live away from home without parental consent; offenders can be given a prison or Borstal sentence.
- Age 18 years – full adult rights including marriage without parental consent; can buy and drink alcoholic drinks in a public house; has the

right to vote; Social Security benefits are available; can have name on council house waiting list; can change surname for personal reasons; can apply for a passport independently.

ADULT LIFE

Adult life begins at the age of 18 and ends at death. It covers a time span of several decades. One way to look at the numerous stages in adult life is to examine what is happening to different age groups. Alongside this it is worth considering the changed and changing face of marriage.

The 18- to 25-year-olds

Who are this group? They are young people at the very beginning of adult life who may still be involved in education or training. Perhaps they are at university or polytechnic and still receiving financial support in the form of grants, loans or assistance from their parents.

In addition, they may have left the parental home and be living in a different part of the country or may be considering home ownership. They may be employed, unemployed and receiving state benefits or travelling round the world. This can be a time of freedom, providing financial stability has been achieved. Finally, people may be considering settling down as couples and perhaps starting a family.

The 25- to 40-year-olds

Who are this group? They are men and women who are married or single, with or without children. They may live as couples or single people. They will usually be concentrating on career progression, hoping to consolidate their experience and looking for promotion. Look at the job adverts in a newspaper. People in this age group seem to be sought after by employers; they have some experience but are still energetic and ambitious.

The 40- to 65-year-olds

Who are this group? They are men and women, with or without children, who may be married, single or have a partner. They may have experienced a career change, have taken early retirement or have been made redundant. Children of people in this age group will be growing up and starting their own careers. The parents of the 40 to 65 age group will be becoming elderly and possibly dependent.

Life events between the ages of 40 and 65

Middle age can be a time of greater security in life. People will have brought up their own children, have greater financial security and will have achieved some, if not all, of their career goals. It should be a time for feeling confident, relaxed and able to enjoy life.

Sometimes people feel negative about being this age. They may feel they have completed the upbringing of children and have perhaps lost a role. They may consider they are faced with the prospect of caring for elderly or infirm relatives just at the point when they would like to enjoy their own lives, free from the constraints of child-rearing. Dissatisfaction with achievements or lack of recognition at work could also be a problem.

Women experience the *menopause* (change of life) any time after 40. This involves a series of hormonal changes which bring about the end of a woman's reproductive life.

It is likely that people in this age group may experience some of the early symptoms of the ageing process. For example, grey hair, long-sightedness and dental problems.

Ill health is also more prevalent at this stage of life and the death rate rises due to an increased incidence of heart disease, cancer and respiratory disorders.

ACTIVITY

Arrange to interview someone in the 40–65 age group. You want to find out how they feel about their age and stage in life. You could ask your parents or grandparents. Before you start, write down your questions under these headings:

- Work/career
- Home life
- Relationships with parents/children
- Social life
- Physical state.

Marriage

Often by the time people are in their twenties they have formed a steady relationship. They may get engaged but live separately, get married or decide to live together as a couple in a stable relationship.

Some reasons why people decide to marry are:

- to escape an unhappy home environment;
- that it is seen as the fashionable thing to do;
- that women think they are 'on the shelf' if they do not get married;
- for companionship.

Some problems which arise within marriage include:

- unrealistic expectations of each other;
- lack of common interests;
- adjusting to different backgrounds and cultures;
- financial difficulties;
- difficulties caused by children or childlessness.

ACTIVITY

One in three marriages ends in divorce. Discuss in groups whether you think it is too easy for couples to obtain a divorce?

OLD AGE

When we discuss old age we are usually referring to people past the age of retirement. In men this is at 65 years and in women it is at 60 years at present, but changes in retirement age are currently under consideration by the government.

An optimistic view of old age was expressed by the poet Robert Browning:

'Grow old along with me
The best is yet to be
The last of life for which the first was made.'

Nowadays, people are living even longer than ever before. Old age can be divided into two categories, early old age (up to 75 years of age) and late old age (beyond 75 years).

Men and women past retirement age form 18 per cent of the population. Women tend to outlive men by about five years on average (see Figure 6.2). The length of time a person can expect to live in years is known as his or her *life expectancy*. Factors which affect life expectancy include:

- the time when a person lives (peace time or war time);
- family background;
- family medical history;
- ethnic group;
- level of wealth;
- male or female;
- lifestyle;
- occupation.

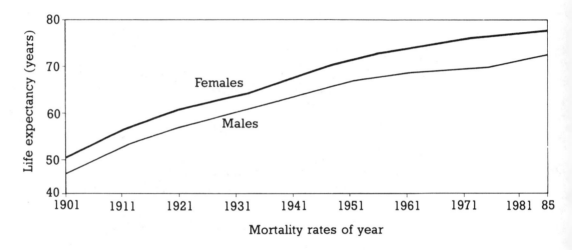

▲ *Figure 6.2 Expectation of life at birth, by sex this century*
Source: Social Trends 19, © Crown copyright 1989. Reproduced courtesy of HMSO.

Physical changes which may occur in old age

Some of the physical changes that are happening throughout life and which become more obvious in old age include the following:

- **Skin changes** – dryness, wrinkling and loss of elasticity.
- **Hair changes** – growth slows, thinning occurs, men may go bald and all body hair goes grey.
- **Eyesight** – long-sightedness may develop when people are in their forties. Sometimes older people find it hard to distinguish between colours. Accomodating from bright light to dark becomes a problem. Side vision becomes narrower. Cataracts and glaucoma can lead to blindness if left untreated.
- **Hearing** – the ability to hear becomes less acute. Appreciation of high-pitch frequencies is lost first.

- **Smell and taste** – these senses become less acute, sometimes causing loss of appetite.
- **Teeth** – may deteriorate quite early on in life if they are not well looked after. Gum disease and decay are major problems. Many old people will have had their teeth extracted or shed them gradually over the years and will be wearing dentures. Carers need to be sensitive to this when providing food and attending to oral hygiene.
- **The lungs and respiratory system** – with age, the lungs become less elastic and respiratory muscles weaken. The exchange of oxygen and carbon dioxide to and from the bloodstream becomes less efficient. Older people are more likely to be affected by physical disorders.
- **The heart and blood vessels** – the efficiency of the heart decreases, blood vessels become less elastic and blood pressure may be raised.
- **The digestive system** – secretions of saliva and digestive juices decrease with advancing age. Food tends to take longer to pass along the digestive tract because the muscles involved have become weaker and less effective. Hence food takes much longer to pass through the body and constipation can become a problem.
- **The urinary system** – the kidneys become less efficient at filtering out waste products effectively. Sometimes frequency of passing urine can be a problem because of reduced bladder capacity and muscle weakness. Women may experience urinary problems relating to gynaecological conditions, such as a prolapse. Men may suffer from enlargement of the prostate gland which may give rise to difficulty in passing urine.
- **The reproductive systems** – in women the menopause will have marked the end of reproductive life. In the post-menopausal years the ovaries will become thicker and smaller, the fallopian tubes get shorter and the uterus and cervix shrink. Vaginal secretions change from acid to alkaline. There is loss of hair on the vulva. The breasts decrease in size.

    In men, reproduction can still take place but the number of viable sperm decreases and sexual arousal is slower.

    However, many old people enjoy sexual activity into late old age and carers need to make provision for this in homes and hospitals.
- **The skeleton and muscles** – between the ages of 20 and 70 a person can lose two inches in height. Total bone mass is reduced and muscles become less flexible. Disfiguration and mobility impairment may occur due to arthritic disease. Posture and mobility are likely to be altered considerably.

This all sounds very negative, and there is no denying that certain aspects of the ageing process can be very troublesome to some individuals, but not to all. Take Emma and Tom, a couple in late old age. He is 86 and she is 79. They look well but both suffer some degree of arthritis. Tom is quite lame due to an arthritic hip. They live in a bungalow without any assistance. They do all their own shopping and cooking, and drive a small car.

Psychological changes which may occur in old age

Personality

It is often said that old people are inflexible and do not adapt well to change. Elderly people derive comfort from familiar surroundings and situations. They are less likely to make mistakes when on their own territory, following long-established routines and behaviour patterns.

Memory

You may notice that some old people easily forget what has happened in the recent past but remember things which have happened several decades ago. This is because of the memory pattern resulting in earlier events being imprinted on the brain by repetition. If old people find their present life dull and uninteresting they may become forgetful by habit.

Learning and intelligence

As people grow older, so their ability to learn may slow down. You may have noticed how it becomes more difficult to remember languages. It is, however, possible to take on new learning in old age. This is demonstrated by the numbers of old people who involve themselves in purposeful learning activities, for example in colleges through The Open University. Old people tend to take longer to absorb new information than younger people but they do not become less intelligent.

Creativity

In later life, people are relieved of the pressure of employment for money and may have time to spend on creative activities of various kinds. Many famous artists have remained productive well into old age – Picasso was still painting at the age of 90.

SOCIAL ASPECTS OF AGEING

The main social aspects of old age are:

- retirement
- family change
- loneliness
- changing roles.

Retirement

Ages of retirement vary world-wide from 55 in Japan to 70 in the USA. Status tends to depend on involvement in a productive occupation. When people leave work they lose their status, the friendship of colleagues, an income and lifestyle. Reduced income can give rise to problems. Economists believe that between 65 and 80 per cent of previous income is necessary in retirement for an equivalent standard of living to be maintained. This does not take into account the effects of inflation.

As retirement marks such a big change in lifestyle, people are advised to plan for it well in advance. Many companies actually put on pre-retirement courses to assist employees with this change.

Family changes

When their children have grown up elderly people will become grandparents and great-grandparents. Old people do have a considerable role to play in the context of the extended family, giving help and support in the form of child care and sometimes even financial help.

Drastic changes are brought about when one partner dies. A woman may have little experience of financial matters, she may not drive or feel confident to attend functions by herself. A man may lack the ability to cook and care for himself and his home.

▲ *Adapting after losing a partner*
© *Chris Kelley, courtesy of Age Concern, England*

Loneliness

This may occur for a variety of reasons amongst older people. They may be isolated in their own homes as they may be unable to get out due to poor mobility or they do not have many visitors. It is also possible for people to feel extremely lonely when they live in institutions. There may be difficulty in forming relationships with other residents and staff. Many people miss their own homes and familiar possessions.

Role reversal

A great worry for old people is that their declining health may cause them to be a burden to others, especially to their children. A situation can arise when an old person becomes totally dependent on one of their children – the roles have been reversed.

OLD AGE AND DISEASE

The ageing body is increasingly subjected to *degenerative diseases*. These are diseases which gradually worsen over time and can be any of the following:

- **Atheroma**   This is a gradual build up of fatty deposits on the walls of the arteries giving rise to coronary heart disease and strokes.
- **Osteoarthritis**   Changes occur in the joints giving rise to pain and loss of mobility.
- **Brain degeneration**   There are two main causes of this: Alzheimer's disease which is excessive degeneration of the nerve cells, and atheroma of the arteries

supplying the brain. Both these changes can lead to a gradual loss of intellectual power.

- **Cancer**   There is an increase in the incidence of many cancers with advancing age.

Ability of the elderly to carry out daily activities

The onset of a degenerative disease can seriously affect an old person's ability to carry out daily functions without assistance. In Chapter 2 you will have seen that most of the support for the elderly is from relatives or friends. If an elderly person needs to move into accommodation where help is on hand, a variety of provision is available, such as:

- sheltered housing where a warden is on call for emergencies and the flats or living units are usually purpose-built;
- private homes for elderly people;
- homes for elderly people run by local authorities;
- geriatric wards in NHS hospitals;
- psycho-geriatric wards in hospitals for the seriously-disturbed elderly.

If an elderly person decides that staying on in their own home is preferable to living in an institution, then support services are available from local authorities. Examples of these services include home helps, meals on wheels, laundry services, mobile libraries and day centres.

Self-help for the elderly

Many people will start making plans and preparations for old age before they reach retirement. For instance, they may be paying into pension schemes or saving in some other way. A move to a smaller house, perhaps in a different area to where they have been living, may also be considered. The extra leisure time needs to be planned for.

DEATH

Dying is usually associated with old age, but it can occur at any age. Death occurs when breathing ceases, the heart stops beating and brain activity ends.

Man is probably the longest-living mammal. It may seem obvious to say that most people die when they are old. However, there are still deaths amongst children and at any age. Indeed the risk of humans dying is highest in the period from conception to birth and the time immediately following birth.

Factors which influence lifespan include the following:

- Women tend to live on average six years longer than men.
- Heredity plays a part as people who live into late old age tend to have a family pattern of longevity.
- Nutrition and lifestyle are also factors, as is companionship into old age.

Less than 2 000 people will reach the age of 100 in any one year. There is only one authenticated case of a person living to the age of 114.

In your home area, research the services for old people provided by the local authority.

1 Produce a map showing where major services are based.

2 Write a summary of your findings.

3 Interview an elderly person in your home area. Find out how much the person uses the services provided and what other provision they would like to see. Write a report on your findings.

4 Compare your findings with members of your group who have carried out their research in other areas. Can a common pattern of provision and need be identified?

ASSIGNMENT 6

When we discuss old age we are usually referring to people past the age of retirement. In the UK at the moment, but currently under review, this is 65 for men and 60 for women. More and more people are living into late old age; 75 years and beyond.

1 Look at the census data in Table 6.2 and answer the following questions.
   a) How many people are expected to survive beyond the age of 85 in the year 2001?
   b) How many more women than men are expected to survive over the age of 85 in the year 2001?
   c) How many more people are surviving beyond the age of 75 in 1991 than in 1951?
   d) Can you think of any reasons why people are living longer today than they did in 1951?
   e) Why do you think women tend to live longer than men?

Census data					Projections	
	1951	1961	1971	1981	1991	2001
Number by age (millions)						
60–64 Women	1.3	1.5	1.7	1.5	1.5	1.4
65–74 Women	2.1	2.3	2.7	2.8	2.8	2.5
Men	1.5	1.6	1.9	2.2	2.2	2.1
Persons	3.6	3.9	4.6	5.0	5.0	4.6
75–84 Women	0.9	1.2	1.4	1.7	1.9	1.9
Men	0.6	0.7	0.7	0.9	1.1	1.1
Persons	1.5	1.8	2.1	2.6	3.0	3.0
85 and over Women	0.2	0.2	0.3	0.4	0.6	0.8
Men	0.1	0.1	0.1	0.1	0.2	0.3
Persons	0.2	0.3	0.5	0.6	0.8	1.0
Total numbers (millions)						
60/65 and over	6.7	7.6	8.8	9.7	10.3	10.1
75 and over	1.7	2.3	2.5	3.1	3.8	4.1
85 and over	0.2	0.3	0.5	0.6	0.8	1.0
Population, all ages (millions)	48.9	51.3	54.0	54.3	55.4	56.4

Table 6.2 *The elderly population of Great Britain by broad age-groups.*
Source: Office of Population Censuses and Surveys, Census Guide 1, Britain's Elderly Population, 1981 Census.

2 As people grow older various changes take place. These are:
- psychological changes;
- physical changes;
- social changes.

Following group discussion and individual research use the headings 'physical', 'psychological' and 'social' to list the changes which may take place with advancing age.

7

Data collection and interpretation

AIMS

- ▶ To learn practical and basic research skills.
- ▶ To integrate theory and skills with practical work.
- ▶ To conduct and present a successful investigation.
- ▶ To learn how to interview and question a sample.
- ▶ To analyse, evaluate and present your research.

SKILLS DEVELOPMENT

The development of skills is an essential part of your training as skills are a vital aspect of your personal development. Those skills which are essential and necessary for success at work are called *common skills*. Certain skills are highlighted for development in different courses. For example, showing a sensitivity to the values, attitudes, cultural beliefs and practices of others is essential for a carer, but an understanding of design skills may not be so important. Other skills you will be introduced to are reporting skills, writing skills, listening skills and verbal skills. You should also be aware than an understanding of how information technology (mainly computers and word-processors) is used is essential to all employment situations in the 1990s.

Common skills

These include:

- communicating;
- self-development (including self-management);
- working with others;
- information gathering;
- identifying problems;
- tackling problems;
- numeracy;
- information processing.

Remember, assignments are not solely concerned with assembling skills, but also with the context within which these skills are developed. Skills are developed and assessed in the context of social care. We will examine these skills (listed above) and how they are assessed later in this chapter.

ACTIVITY

What practical skills do you think are necessary for you to develop in order to care for an elderly dependent person?

List them and compare them with the practical skills you think are necessary to support a person who is deaf.

CONDUCTING AND PRESENTING A SUCCESSFUL INVESTIGATION

Planning the assignment

- Select the assignment topic.
- Decide on your approach, for example, observation or questionnaire.
- Formulate your plan – how are you going to carry out the research, collect data, etc.?
- Carry out the project to collect the data and information.
- Analyse and interpret the data.
- Write up the assignment.
- Present your findings to your colleagues.

Data gathering

However you choose to collect your information and data, there are certain activities that are common:

- You must know where to locate the data and make arrangements to collect it.
- The information must be collected and recorded in a form suitable for analysis.

Getting access to data can be a problem for students carrying out an assignment. You may often find that the individuals or groups that you want to study may be unwilling to provide information. So, bear in mind how accessible information is before you spend too much time on the assignment.

Where do you look for information resources?

Information should be available from the following sources:

- class notes and handouts;
- articles in the press and magazines;
- books in your college and local library;
- videos and TV programmes;
- agencies or places relevant to the assignment, for example, day centres, hospitals or play groups;
- information you have gathered as a result of writing letters to organisations, etc.

The information and data you gather must be relevant to your assignment. Do not collect information just because you find it interesting.

If you use a sample, say users of a day centre, make sure that the sample is a good one. A sample of users of the centre on a Monday only would not give you enough data to generalise about all users.

Record your data properly and in particular state the conditions under which you gathered the information.

How can you record your data and information?

- **Log book** — This is the simplest method. Recording of interviews, books read and information gathered can be recorded in a simple exercise book.
- **On tape** — Tapes are acceptable for recording interviews and recording important data (in the form of verbal notes) from journals or books. One drawback of tape recording

interviews is the amount of time needed to transcribe the information.

- **Interview notes**   This method is useful if you are carrying out open-ended interviews in which you are encouraging the person you are interviewing to express opinions or elaborate on a subject.
- **On video**   Lightweight video cameras are excellent for recording information.

Before you decide what information to collect you should consider the following points:

- How long have you been given to carry out the assignment?
- How available is the data and information?
- How accessible is the data or information?
- Can you do all you want to do in the time given?
- Have you the skills to carry out the project?

There are a number of reasons why you may experience difficulty in carrying out the assignment. The first of these difficulties is selecting a suitable topic or field of study and the second difficulty is managing your time.

Time management

Let us suppose that you are going to carry out a survey of parents of young children who use a local day nursery to find out what service they require.

Activity description	Estimated duration in weeks
Discussion with tutor	1
Discussion with nursery	1
First draft of questionnaire	1
Discussion with tutor and finalisation of questionnaire	1
Administer questionnaire	2
Analyse data	1
Write up report	2
Total	**9**

Table 7.1 A time plan

You can see from the list of activities given in Table 7.1 that for a simple survey you need to think in terms of at least nine weeks. Planning your time is a very important aspect of carrying out assignments.

HOW TO GATHER INFORMATION

Everybody observes other people at work or in other social situations. There is an important difference, however, between the observations of the student carrying out an assignment and someone observing drinkers in a pub. Why is this? Because students must organise and analyse their data in a logical, systematic and sensitive manner. The ordinary person relies primarily on memory, but students attempt to keep written descriptions of what they see. For this reason, students are forced to think of systematic ways to conduct their research.

Observation

One method used to find out about how people behave is to observe them. For example, if you wanted to find out how residents behave in the dining room of a day unit how would you go about it?

You could get a part-time job in the unit, sit down with the residents, eat a meal with them and observe their behaviour. Alternatively, you could visit the unit, sit apart from the residents and watch what they do.

The first method (*participant observation*) has a high degree of interaction and the second method (*non-participant observation*) a low degree of interaction. Which method do you think would yield the data likely to give the deepest insight into the behaviour of the diners?

ACTIVITY

What are the dangers of participant observation?
Next time you are in a work placement in a residential establishment, observe the residents in the rest-room or TV room. Who do they sit with? Do they always sit in the same chair? Which resident has control of the TV? Who makes the tea?

Will people behave differently when they know they are being watched?
Do you think that if you are a participant observer that there is a danger of becoming too involved in the activities of the group you are observing?
How long did it take you to gather enough data to understand what was going on?
Did you fully understand what was going on?
Discuss your views with your class colleagues.

Interviews and questionnaires

Instead of observing what people do, would you get more relevant data if you ask what they are doing or ask them their views on what they are doing? A *questionnaire* is simply a list of questions which provides a relatively fast, effective and cheap method of obtaining information. The personal interview can be regarded as a face-to-face, interpersonal situation in which the interviewer's questions are designed to obtain answers which are relevant to the assignment or research.

A good questionnaire requires a lot of thought and planning. You must ask yourself:

- What questions are you going to ask?
- Who are you going to ask?
- How are you going to record your answers?
- What are you going to do with the results?

Before you construct a questionnaire you must carry out some background reading and research into the subject of your assignment. This will give you some ideas of the questions that should be asked. You should read books, journals and leaflets to gain some general ideas about your assignment. It might also be useful to read other research projects which involved questionnaires and other publications and statistics relevant to your area of study.

If you want to draw up tables and graphs from your data you will need to ask questions which allow for only a limited number of answers. You can then add up the number of people who give each answer and look for patterns.

Structured or unstructured interviews?

There are two main types of interview; *structured* interviews and *unstructured* interviews. The structured form of interview is one in which the questions, their wording and their sequence are fixed and identical for each *respondent* (the person who replies to the questions). Any variations which appear in the responses can be attributed to the actual differences between the respondents and not to variations in the interview.

Why carry out a structured interview?

Structured interviews provide an objective exercise and the tendencies towards bias are less than with observation or unstructured interviews. A major advantage is that the information can be easily coded and analysed by computer.

It is important to give a lot of thought to the questionnaire, as structured interviews are only as good as the questions asked. It is also important to frame the questions in a language that the respondents will understand. Questions should be framed so as to avoid woolly generalisations. They should not be biased towards encouraging the respondents to give an answer that you want them to give. An example of a structured questionnaire is shown in Figure 7.1.

How often do you watch football on television?

Never. ☐

Once a month or less. ☐

Two or three times a month. ☐

Every week. ☐

How much money do you spend on petrol each month?

Less than £10. ☐

£10–20. ☐

£21 or more. ☐

Why don't you go to the cinema?

Don't like what's showing. ☐

Prefer to watch it on video. ☐

It costs too much money. ☐

Worried about the cigarette smoke. ☐

Other reasons (please state). _____

_____

_____

▲ *Figure 7.1 Example of a structured questionnaire*

There are many problems with questions. Some may be unclear, or use words that the respondent may not understand.

Read the following examples and rewrite each question to overcome the problems.

Leading questions

These questions encourage the respondent to say 'Yes'. Therefore, these questions are biased.

1 Do you think that women should not start work until their children are old enough?

2 Don't you agree that there is too much sex on television?

Questions which presume

These questions presume that the respondent has done the actions defined in the question.

3 When did you last go to the seaside?

4 How many cups of coffee have you had?

Double-barrelled questions

These are questions with more than one part.

5 Do you think that the college should spend less money on books and more on the dining room?

6 Do you think that there is too much violence at football matches and that this is responsible for the lowering of standards in society?

Why carry out an unstructured interview?

The least structured form of interviewing is the *unstructured*, or *non-directive*, interview (see Figure 7.2). Respondents are given no direction from the interviewer. They are encouraged to relate their experience, and to reveal their opinions and attitudes as they see fit. It allows the respondents to express their opinions as well as answer the questions. The respondents can let you know their real feelings about the subject of the question and, therefore, tend to answer more freely and fully.

Your task is to discover as many specific kinds of conflicts and tensions between child and parent as possible. The four areas of possible conflict we want to explore are listed in question 3 in Figure 7.2. The first two questions are to allow you to build up a rapport with the respondent.

1 What sort of problems do teenagers have in getting along with their parents?

2 What sort of disagreements do you have with your parents?

3 Have you ever had any disagreement with either parent over:
   a) using the family car;
   b) friends of the same sex;
   c) dating;
   d) smoking?

▲ *Figure 7.2 Example of an unstructured interview*

When interviewing, do you think that there are situations when the respondent might feel inhibited? Discuss with you class colleagues the effect on an interview that the following scenarios might have.

- A white interviewer and a black respondent.
- A male interviewer and a female respondent.

What do you have to do to encourage people to complete and return the questionnaires?
With all surveys there is the problem of people who may refuse to fill in your questionnaire or simply forget to do so. This makes your results less accurate. If your response rate is low what can you do to improve it?

There are various methods, including the following, that you can use to improve the response rate:

- **Follow-up** — Write or telephone the people who have not responded.
- **Length of questionnaire** — The shorter the better, as longer questionnaires tend not to be answered.
- **Who gave out the questionnaire?** — If the respondents know you or the college, then they are likely to reply. However, where questions are of a confidential nature this may not be the case and in these instances you must stress confidentiality in your introductory letter.
- **Introductory letter** — An appeal to the respondents to emphasise that they would be helping the interests of everyone seems to produce the best results.
- **Method of return** — A stamped addressed envelope produces the best results.
- **Format of the questionnaire** — A title that will arouse interest helps, as does an attractive and clear layout with plenty of room for hand-written answers.

The self-administered questionnaire

The self-administered questionnaire, as a method, is cheaper than others and avoids the problems, such as bias, associated with the use of interviewers. The self-administered questionnaire has some positive advantages. People are more likely to express socially-unacceptable attitudes and feelings when answering a questionnaire alone than when confronted by an interviewer. The greater the anonymity the more honest the response. Aside from the greater honesty that they may produce, self-administered questionnaires also have the advantage of giving a respondent more time to think.

This type of survey gives no opportunity for the respondent to probe beyond the answer. Therefore, the questions should be simple and straightforward, and be understood with the help of minimal, printed instructions.

The principles of interviewing

The first step in interviewing is to get the respondent to co-operate and provide the desired information. This can be done by following a few simple guidelines:

- The person you are interviewing needs to feel that the interview will be pleasant and satisfying.

- Interviewers should present themselves as being understanding and easy to talk to.
- The people being interviewed need to feel that the study is worthwhile.
- The interviewer also needs to overcome the respondents' suspicions.
- The interviewer should explain in a friendly manner the purpose of the study and the confidential nature of the interview.

How can you put people at ease?
- Tell the respondent who you are and who you represent.
- Tell the respondent what you are doing in a way that will make them interested in what you are doing.
- Tell the respondent how and why they were chosen to be interviewed. Any instructions should be brief.
- Create a relationship of confidence between yourself and the person you are interviewing.

WHAT KIND OF QUESTIONS SHOULD YOU ASK?

In the previous section we focused on how to collect information. In this section we shall look at the different kind of questions and their content as they provide the foundation of all questionnaires.

There are basically two types of questions: *factual questions* and *opinion* or *attitude questions*.

Factual questions

Factual questions elicit *objective* information. The most common type of factual questions obtain information such as sex, age, marital status, education or income of respondents. An example of such a question would be:

'At what age did you leave school?'

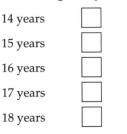

14 years

15 years

16 years

17 years

18 years

Please tick the appropriate box

Other factual questions could elicit information about a respondent's social environment, for example, 'How many people are living in your household?' or their leisure activities, 'How often do you go to the cinema?'

Opinion or attitude questions

Opinion or attitude questions are more difficult to construct. Before we examine how to develop an opinion or attitude question we must first examine the difference between an 'attitude' and an 'opinion'. An *attitude* is the sum total of a person's prejudices, ideas, fears and convictions about any specific topic. *Opinions* are the verbal expression of attitudes.

To obtain data about factual matters or attitudes, you can ask open-ended or close-ended questions.

Close-ended questions

In *close-ended questions* respondents are given a set of answers from which they are asked to choose one that closely represents their views, for example:

'Caring is a female job.'

Strongly agree	Agree	Disagree	Strongly disagree

Please tick the appropriate box.

Close-ended questions are easy to ask and quick to be answered, and their analysis is straightforward. Answers can be more elaborate than open-ended questions. For example:

'Do you feel that you are really part of your class group?'

Really a part of my class. ☐

Included in most ways. ☐

Included in some ways, but not in others. ☐

Don't feel that I really belong. ☐

Don't fit in with any class group. ☐

Don't know. ☐

Please tick the appropriate box.

Open-ended questions

Open-ended questions are not followed by any kind of specified choice; respondents' answers are recorded in full. For example, the question 'What do you personally feel are the most important problems the government should try to tackle?', is an open-ended question. The virtue of this type of question is that the respondent can express their thoughts freely, spontaneously and in their own way.

What type of questions should you use?

In what situations should you use the different types of questions. The following points should be considered:

- **The objectives of the questionnaire**   Close-ended questions are suitable when you want to find out if the respondent agrees or disagrees with a point of view. If you want to find out how the respondent arrived at this view, an open-ended question is more appropriate.
- **How much the respondent knows about the topic in question**   Open-ended questions give you the opportunity to find out how much the respondents know about the topic. Obviously, it is futile to ask any questions that are beyond the experience of the respondent.
- **Communication**   How easily can the contents of the answers be communicated by the respondent?
- **Motivation**   What is the extent of the respondent's motivation to answer the questions?

Design and structure of the questionnaire

Rating

One of the most common formats for questions in social science surveys is the rating scale. Here, respondents are asked to make a judgement in terms of strength of feeling, for example:

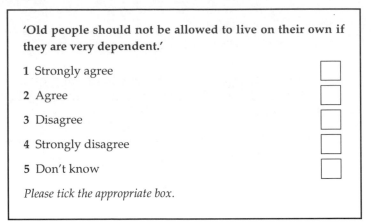

'Old people should not be allowed to live on their own if they are very dependent.'

1 Strongly agree ☐

2 Agree ☐

3 Disagree ☐

4 Strongly disagree ☐

5 Don't know ☐

Please tick the appropriate box.

These responses reflect the intensity of the respondent's judgement.

Double-barrelled questions

Try not to ask double-barrelled questions, i.e. those questions that have two or more questions in one. For example: **'Would you say that most people are like you and can be trusted?'**

This question includes two questions. The problem with it is that it is likely to confuse respondents who may agree with one aspect of the question and disagree with the other.

Selecting a sample

To be fully comprehensive and accurate a survey should be filled in by everyone to whom it applies. For example, if you wish to find out about how users of a cinema feel about it, you should ask every user. This would, however, take too long and would be very expensive. You must therefore question a sample of the users.

How big the sample should be will depend on what you want to do with the results. If you want to generalise, then you must interview as large a sample as possible. If you only interview six mothers who use a day nursery on a Friday, you cannot state that their views represent those of the users on the other days of the week. If you want to generalise about users of the day nursery, you must interview a sample who use it *every* day.

Asking your friends in a pub about drinking would be likely to give you a biased set of answers. You would only have the views of your pub friends who probably all drink.

ACTIVITY

You wanted to find out how people in your locality feel about their local councillors and it was only possible to interview people in the High Street one morning at 11 a.m. What type of people might be missed out? How would you go about getting a fully representative sample?

Covering letters

After you have selected your sample and constructed the questionnaire, the next step is to write a covering letter for postal-type questionnaires or an introductory statement for other types of surveys. This letter or statement should explain the purpose of the survey. The statement must succeed in overcoming any resistance or prejudice the respondent may have against the survey.

The letter or statement must include:

- details of the organisation sponsoring the study, for example the college;
- it must explain the purpose of the study;
- explain why it is important that the respondent should answer the questions;
- assure them that the information they provide will be treated in the strictest confidence.

ACTIVITY

1 Design a questionnaire to find out the age, sex, qualifications and attitude or opinion of your class colleagues to a local football team or disco venue.

2 When you have designed the questionnaire, write a covering letter or introductory statement explaining the purpose of the survey. This should explain why they should participate and tell them how you will treat the information obtained.

Literature search

Most assignment work involves the use of published literature. You will be expected to read books and articles from journals. It is not the intention of this book to teach you how to use the library, but to help you get to know where you can access information.

The catalogue of books in the library will be classified by author and class number or title. Journals and periodicals are usually listed in alphabetical order.

When collecting material for an assignment or similar piece of work you must note in full the details of each item consulted. Write out details on cards or slips of paper which you can file in alphabetical order until you need them to write your list of references at the end of your report.

Useful sources for social care students

- *Social Service Abstracts*   Summaries of selected documents prepared by the DHSS Library.
- *Social Trends*   Published annually by the Central Statistics Office in London.
- *Population Trends*   Published by the Office of Population, Census and Survey and available from HMSO.
- *British National Film and Video Catalogue*   From the British Film Institute.
- *A Handbook of Research for the Helping Profession*   C. Sutton, Routledge and Kegan Paul, 1987.
- *Older People, A Resource List for Social Work Trainees*   CCETSW, 1988.
- *Health Care in Multi-Racial Britain*   P. Mares, A. Hanly and C. Baxter, Health Education Council, 1985.

Journals

- *Care Weekly* Data on residential and day care. Published weekly by Hutton Wild Communications Ltd, London.
- *Community Care* Articles on a wide variety of social care subjects. Published weekly by Reed Business Publishing Group, Surrey.
- *Social Work Today* The journal of the Association of Social Workers. Published weekly.
- *Nursing Times* Articles on nursing and social care. Published weekly by Macmillan Magazines, London.
- *New Home Economics* Published ten times a year by Forbes Publications Ltd, London.
- *New Scientist* Published weekly by Holborn Publishing Group, London.
- *Nursery World* Published weekly by Nursery World Ltd, London.
- *Open Mind* A mental health magazine published every two months by MIND, the National Association of Mental Health, London.
- *Social Studies Review* Published monthly by Philip Arthur, Oxfordshire.

Sources of information are classified into *primary*, *secondary* and *tertiary*:

- Primary sources are the first publication of a work and appear in journals, reports, government publications, conference reports and directories.
- Secondary sources are the indexing and classification of primary sources. These appear in textbooks, subject abstracts and monographs.
- Tertiary sources facilitate the location of primary and secondary sources. These are handbooks, bibliographies and encyclopedias.

ACTIVITY

Classify the following sources of information.

1 *Social Service Abstracts*, published by the DHSS.

2 Challis, D. (1988) 'Community Care for the Elderly: An Urban Experiment' *British Journal of Social Work*, Vol. 16.

3 *Encyclopedia Britannica*.

HOW TO RECORD AND PRESENT DATA

Information or data can be presented in the form of:

- diagrams
- graphs
- pie charts
- tables.

Each of the four different methods helps you to present information in an understandable and logical way.

Diagrams

Diagrams are a way of presenting a lot of information in picture form. A good diagram will help you cut down on the amount of writing you would otherwise have to do to describe the information presented in the diagram.

▲ *Figure 7.3 Diagram of old people's home*

Examine the diagram of the old people's home (Figure 7.3) and answer the following questions.

1 How many rooms are single bedrooms

2 How many day rooms are there?

3 How many dining areas are there?

4 Do the staff have a rest-room?

5 Does the manager have an office?

6 Are there facilities for residents to prepare a meal themselves?

7 Is there easy access for disabled clients to enter or leave the building?

8 Are there any special facilities for disabled clients?

Graphs

Information can be presented in a variety of graphical forms. Graphs can be used to show changes in a particular variable over a given period of time. The graph can be used to reinforce points made in writing.

Bar graph

Examples of bar graphs are shown in Figures 7.4 and 7.5.

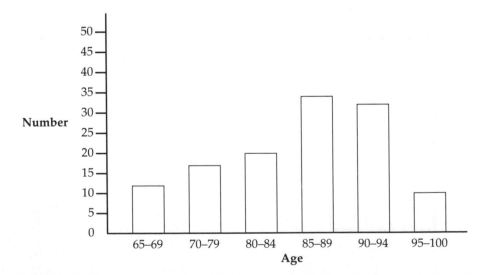

▲ *Figure 7.4 Graph to show the number of elderly people admitted to residential care in Downside Local Authority, by age, for the year 1991.*

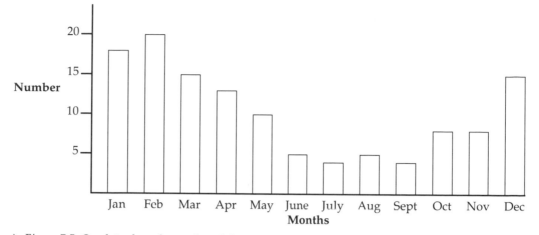

▲ *Figure 7.5 Graph to show the number of elderly people admitted to residential care in Downside Local Authority for the year 1991*

ACTIVITY

Compare the data in the two bar graphs (Figures 7.4 and 7.5) and answer these questions.

1 How many people were admitted to residential care during the months of January to March?

2 Why do you think that the number of clients admitted during the months of January, February and March are so high?

3 Why do you think so few people in the 65 to 80 age range are in residential care?

4 What effect has the high percentage of over 80-year-old people in residential care have on the operation of the homes?

ACTIVITY

Construct a bar graph from the following data.

Children (by age) on child protection register at 31 March 1991

Age	Number
< 1 year	25
1–4	200
5–8	167
9–12	100
13–15	75
16>	8

Bar-line graph

Another simple and clear method to present data is by using a bar-line graph (sometimes called a stick graph). For example, a bar-line graph could be used to show the number of meals on wheels delivered by time of delivery (see Figure 7.6).

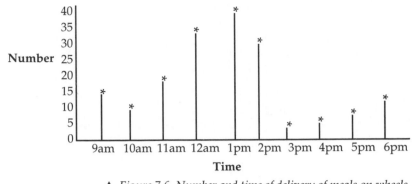

▲ *Figure 7.6 Number and time of delivery of meals on wheels*

1 From the data shown in Table 7.2, construct a bar or bar-line graph.

Month	Number
January	100
February	89
March	84
April	81
May	70
June	60
July	55
August	50
September	63
October	70
November	75
December	85
Total	**882**

Table 7.2 *Referrals for home help to Downside Social Services Department for the year 1991*

2 Why do you think that there are so few referrals in June, July and August?

3 In what month was the largest percentage of referrals made?

Line graph

A line graph is another useful way to illustrate increasing or decreasing values. Examples are given in Figures 7.7 and 7.8.

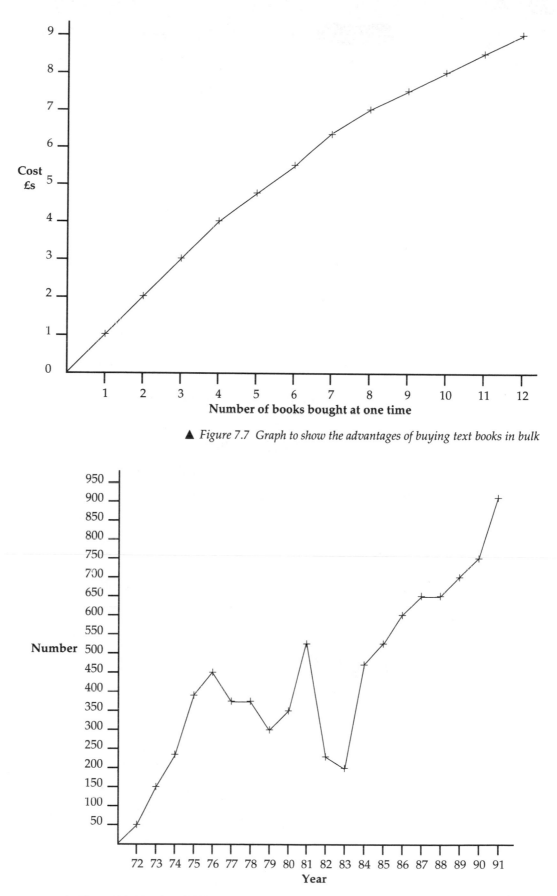

▲ Figure 7.7 Graph to show the advantages of buying text books in bulk

▲ Figure 7.8 Number of children on the children at risk register, by calendar year, from 1972

ACTIVITY

Look at the graph in Figure 7.7 and answer the following questions.

1 What is the cost of one book?

2 What is the cost of five books?

3 What is the cost of seven books?

4 What is the cost of ten books?

How do you arrive at a percentage

Look at Table 7.2, on page 138, which shows the number of home help referrals. We can work out the percentage of referrals for the month of April as follows:

- Divide the number of referrals for April by the total number of referrals for the year:

$$\frac{\text{Number of referrals in April}}{\text{Total referrals for the year}} \quad \frac{81}{882} = 0.092.$$

- Then multiply by 100 to obtain the percentage

$$0.092 \times 100 = 9.2.$$

- The percentage of referrals for the month of April was 9.2 per cent.

ACTIVITY

Work out the percentage of home help referrals for the month of June.

ACTIVITY

Have a look at the information in Table 7.3. Then copy the graph axes opposite and draw one of the types of graph (bar, bar-line or line) using the data in the table.

Age	Number	Percentage
Under 20	19	1.0
20–29	163	9.0
30–39	433	24.5
40–49	643	36.0
50–59	418	23.5
60+	101	6.0
Total	**1777**	**100.0**

Table 7.3 *Community auxiliary nurses by age*

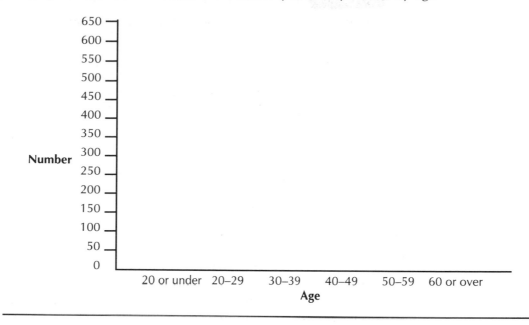

Graph to show the number of community auxiliary nurses by age

Pie charts

A pie chart is a visual presentation which breaks down a total figure into different components. Look at the pie chart in Figure 7.9 which illustrates the percentages of students attending social care courses at a college, aiming to achieve various qualifications.

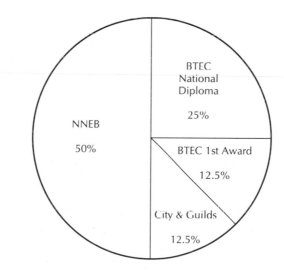

▲ *Figure 7.9 Percentage of students attending social care courses leading to various qualifications*

The percentage figures were derived from the following data:

Qualification	Number of students
NNEB	200
BTEC National Diploma	100
BTEC 1st Award	50
City & Guilds	50
Total	**400**

Construct a pie chart to illustrate the following data:

Qualifications of staff	Number	Percentage
CQSW	86	9.9
Cert. Social Service (CSS)	180	20.8
Management	20	2.3
BTEC	26	3.0
Other	23	2.6
None	532	61.4
Total	**867**	**100**

Tables

Tables enable you to show much more data than, for instance, in a bar graph or bar-line graph. The table below shows the response rate to a postal questionnaire which was sent to a sample of home helps (Group A) and a sample of auxiliary nurses (Group B) in a national survey.

	Group A		Group B	
	No.	%	No.	%
Questionnaires distributed	1302	100.0	1961	100.0
Questionnaires returned	1170		1482	
Incompleted questionnaires	133		144	
Total analysed	1037	79.6	1338	68.2

Table 7.4 *Response rates to a postal questionnaire*

From the data in Table 7.4 we can see that although Group B were sent more questionnaires (1 961) the percentage response (68.2%) was lower than in Group A (79.6%).

NOTE TAKING

Note taking is a very important aspect of your work and it is a skill that you must develop. It will provide you with a written record of what you have been studying or information that you have collected. To be useful these notes must be accurately taken and presented. You should take notes in a consistent format. In class, a looseleaf binder is better than an exercise book because you can rearrange your notes for tutorials or revision. However, if you are observing a situation and taking notes, or interviewing someone, than a less-obtrusive method is best – perhaps a small notebook or even a tape recorder.

Recording key points

In class or when carrying out a survey, you should take brief, intelligible notes that will allow you to recall the important key points later. You need to capture the important ideas and the line of argument. In class, concentrate on following the flow of an argument or lecture and just jot down any key points within a coherent structure.

Be familiar with the topic

In order to make the best use of any lecture you should be familiar with the topic. You can do this by reading as much as you can in advance. Ask questions of the lecturer if you do not understand any point or want elaboration. Supplement your class notes with notes made from books.

The same applies when preparing to interview someone. Read around the subject and plan the interview. Work out what notes you will want to make.

Before reading a book or article ask yourself what you expect to gain from it.

- Why are you reading the book?
- What are you interested in?
- Skim through the book to see which parts are most relevant to you.
- Note the title, author and date of publication (most recent edition).
- Read the introduction, examine the contents page and check the range of research by reading the bibliography which will also give you suggestions for further reading.
- Read the chapter headings and look through the index.

All the above will help you to gain a general impression of the type of book you are reading. The date of publication will give you an idea of the historical context in which the book was written. Reading the introduction ensures that you understand the author's intention in writing the article or book. The index might give you ideas as to the type of notes you wish to make.

Use your own words

Make notes in your own words. The process of converting the ideas in the book into your own language will also ensure that you understand the content. Add your own comments where appropriate and also make a note of any relevant page numbers. Knowing the page number is important for a variety of reasons. First, you can find the material again quickly. For example, White – 27 means that the notes came from page 27 of White's book. Secondly, when you copy material word for word from a publication you should include it in quote marks and must also let the reader know the page number of the book or journal you quoted from by using an appropriate acknowledgement.

How do you organise information?

What do you do with the information you have found or gathered? You can use a card to record the information but in many cases a computer is even better. The card or computer should contain the following information:

- title
- author
- publisher
- place of publication
- date of publication.

You will also have in your file your own comments on the article or chapter and a summary of the main points.

- To reference the title of a book or article by key word. For example, *Domiciliary Care of the Elderly* could become
Elderly, Domiciliary Care of the
This allows you to file the data under the key word 'Elderly'.
- The author's name and date of publication. For example, Clarke, J. L. (1986).
- The source of information. For example, *Social Work Today*, Vol. 22, No. 12, 15 Nov 1990, pp. 26–8.

ANALYSING AND EVALUATING INFORMATION AND DATA

One important function of analysis is to communicate the results of your findings. An even more important reason for analysis is to show that the assignment measures up to the necessary standards set for the work.

- Plan your analysis at the beginning of the assignment so that data gathering can be organised around the analysis.
- Make sure you are thoroughly familiar with the methods of analysis described in this chapter.
- Decide which methods of analysis you are going to use.
- Do not use analytical methods for the sake of them. Choose appropriate methods. Sophisticated methods are not always the best. If your data is poor no amount of analysis can improve it.
- Write your conclusions down as you go along so it is clear what you are saying. Discuss them with your tutor and review them after discussion.

ACTIVITY

How do you analyse closed or structured questions?

The question

Do you think that caring is a female job?

Strongly agree ☐

Agree ☐

Disagree ☐

Strongly disagree ☐

Draw up a tally chart of answers. The tally may look like this:

The results

Strongly agree	JHT	JHT	II			12
Agree	JHT	JHT	JHT			15
Disagree	JHT	JHT	JHT	JHT	JHT	25
Strongly disagree	JHT	JHT	III			13

Summarise these results and also illustrate them in a graph form of your choosing.

PRESENTING YOUR FINDINGS

Write fully about every stage of your research. Describe the background to your survey in detail – why you set out to examine that particular topic and how you planned the research. At the end of your research (possibly in an appendix) include a copy of any questionnaire you may have used, explain why you asked each question and what you hoped to find out with it.

Explain in detail how you selected your sample and any problems you encountered. Analyse any problems with your assignment in general and explain how these may have influenced your results.

You must present your assignment in a clear and logical way. To put it simply, there must be a beginning to the report, a middle and an end. The end usually covers your conclusions and recommendations.

Most presentations of your work will be in the written form, but you may have negotiated with your tutor to present your finding on tape, video or photographs, or a mixture of methods.

Always prepare a rough draft of your report as this will help you decide on the best method of arranging your material. You should be prepared to redraft your report several times before you present it in a final form. Make sure you check spellings, that the sentences read well and that your ideas and arguments flow well.

Your final presentation is very important. A typed or word-processed version is preferable but otherwise write neatly and clearly with a good quality pen. Pay attention to the layout and use the same paper for the whole report unless you are using hand-drawn, detailed graphs which should be on appropriate, squared graph paper.

Elements and order of a written report

- **Title page** The title of your assignment.
- **Contents** A list of paragraph or section headings.
- **List of tables/graphs** The titles of tables or graphs.
- **Body of the report** Introduction – what you did – your sample – your findings, etc.
- **Conclusions** Summary of the assignment, i.e. what you have learned.
- **Appendices** Any copies of questionnaires or articles, leaflets, etc.
- **List of references** Books, journals, articles quoted in the body of the report, etc.
- **Bibliography** List of books or articles you have read as background research.

Work placement – the real thing

AIMS

▶ To understand the advantages of work placement and its value to you.

▶ To assess the best placement for your requirements.

▶ To prepare for your placement.

▶ To realise the importance of keeping a record of what occurs on the placement.

▶ To learn how to record facts, tasks and progress.

WHAT IS A WORK PLACEMENT AND WHY DO IT?

Students on foundation social care courses may have had no experience of caring for people in a formal setting. Some of you may have done some voluntary work, looked after aged relatives or babysat for friends or relatives. Formal work-placement experience will give you the opportunity to experience working with different kinds of people – elderly people, children or people with a handicap – and will also allow you to practise some of the skills you will learn in college.

Work placements will also give you the opportunity to acquire a realistic picture of the range and types of services available to people living in your community. They will also give you the chance to experience the type of work you might like to do later on in a career.

Your placement is an active learning experience. It will allow you to relate the theories you learn and discuss in college to the work place and is a key element in the achievement of your course aims. You will be able to observe good practice, write reports and develop your skills (especially communication skills), all of which will increase your confidence and help you to evaluate your own abilities.

Why have work placement experience?

The advantages are:

- to participate in work activities;
- to acquire a realistic picture of social care work;
- to relate theory to practice;
- to observe good practice;
- to gain confidence;
- to demonstrate your level of skill.

Understanding the job

You will be given the opportunity to understand the job of caring for someone through carrying out basic caring tasks and observing other staff. It is important that you use this opportunity to extend your understanding of what is happening in the work place by discussing things you see and hear with college staff, agency staff and your student colleagues.

Levels of competence

To begin with you may work alongside other staff but as you gain confidence you will be allowed to do simple tasks. The amount of responsibility you will have at each stage will depend on your performance and relationship with your supervisor. An important element of this experience will be the opportunity to demonstrate appropriate levels of competence in certain skills. The skills you will be allowed to practice will have been agreed by you with your tutor and work-place supervisor, and will differ according to the type of work experience.

Responding to different client groups

Placement experience will enable you to gain an understanding of a client group and begin to recognise their particular needs. This will allow you to respond in a professional and sensitive manner. Your experience will also allow you to develop relationships with staff and clients as individuals and as members of a group. You will have the opportunity to work as part of a team, develop self-awareness and be responsive to constructive criticism.

Assessment

Your college or school tutor will visit you a number of times during your placement to observe you at work. Your tutor will be interested to see how you put into practice the skills you have learned at school or college and the relationships you develop with clients and co-workers in the placement. Your tutor will spend some time talking to your supervisor about your involvement and progress.

WHAT PLACEMENT IS BEST FOR YOU?

The availability of placements will depend on where you live, for instance if you live in a large city then you may have a wide choice, but if you live in a small town or rural area you may be more limited in your opportunities. Placements may be obtained either in public, private or voluntary agencies.

What are the available placements

The types of placements usually available to students on basic caring courses include:

- residential homes for elderly people, children, mentally ill people, and people who are mentally or physically disabled;
- day centres for elderly people, children, mentally ill people and people who are mentally or physically disabled;
- services for children, such as day nurseries, nursery schools, nursery units, special schools, play groups and creches;
- hospitals for elderly people, mentally disabled people and special children's wards in hospitals;
- private homes as a nanny or mother's help;
- home care, such as in a home help service or community nursing service;
- miscellaneous, for example, in Citizens' Advice Bureaux or police stations.

How can you find out what placement opportunities are available in your locality?

1 With your fellow students you should survey and identify all the possible establishments and agencies that may be able to offer you a placement. List all the relevant schools, nurseries, play groups, homes for old people, voluntary agencies, day centres, hospitals, etc.
This information could be displayed in a number of ways on a local map. For example, identify hospitals with a red marker, day centres with a green marker; or you could choose different symbols to identify different agencies on the map (see below).

2 Using this information produce a general file of possible work experiences and their location. Find out how difficult it is to travel to each, and record this and other information that would be helpful to you in making a choice of placement.

3 When you have done this discuss your options with your tutor and other students.

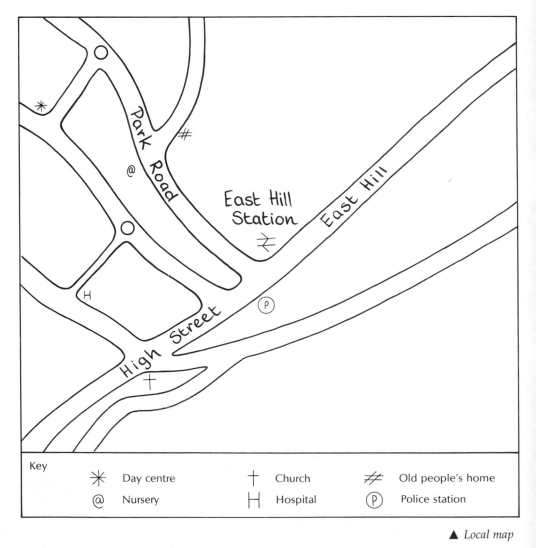

▲ *Local map*

Factors to consider

- Your previous experience.
- Your special interests.
- Your preferred client group.
- The objectives of the placement.
- Whether the placement is well within your capabilities.
- Whether the placement will be difficult but a challenge you want to try for.
- Whether the placement will be an entirely new experience.
- Your tutor's comments on the placement and your abilities/aptitudes.
- The availability of a placement.
- The distance from home.
- The cost of travel.

PREPARING FOR PLACEMENT

Work experience is an important part of all caring courses and needs careful consideration and preparation. You may have a strong preference about which group of clients you would like to work with. Very often, working with children is seen as the most attractive option, but it is a good idea to acquire as wide an experience of as many client groups as possible before making a final career choice.

Most students enjoy their placement; it is for many the 'real' part of their course. Some students, however, do not get as much from their placement as they should for a number of reasons. Therefore, it is important that you understand and adopt some basic principles to help you begin your placement well and make it a worthwhile experience. Do not be too disappointed if your first choice of work experience is not available.

Your appearance

Your personal appearance is most important. Ask yourself the following questions:

- What clothes do I need to wear?
- Do I need any special clothing?
- Does the college or the placement supply special clothing or do I have to buy it myself?
- What do I look like?
- What should I look like in the placement?

What is sensible and appropriate clothing or jewellery? Think about the tasks that you may be called upon to carry out in your placement. Loose, bright jewellery, such as ear rings, will attract young children in a play group or nursery. They may pull any jewellery and injure you. Working in a home for elderly people may involve you in helping to lift someone out of bed or a chair, so wearing high-heeled shoes could cause you to slip.

▲ *What do you look like?*

The preliminary visit

Going on a placement may cause you some anxiety, but your tutor will usually have discussed the placement with you and identified for you the member of staff in the placement who will be responsible for you while you are there.

You should make arrangements to see this member of staff before the placement begins. This is to discuss what is expected of you and what you expect of the placement. You can discuss what hours you are expected to work, what tasks you will be involved with and who you will report to on the first day of the placement.

This preliminary visit is a crucial stage in preparing for placement. You must get hold of the information you need to perform well. Make sure you know:

- **who** your supervisor is;
- **when** you are to attend;
- **what** you are to do;
- **what** you are **not** to do.

Because you need to gain experience of actually working with and caring for people, your tutors will probably obtain placements for you where you are allowed to work with staff. The staff and the clients will therefore be dependent on you so you must *always act in a professional manner*. Good timekeeping and attendance is very important, as is a willingness to observe, ask questions and listen.

Once your placement is confirmed:

- read about your client group;
- go through your course work and check out the relevant notes;
- discuss your placement with students and college staff.

What rights and responsibilities do you have while on placement?

You have the **right** to be protected by the current health and safety legislation while you are on placement. You, however, have the **responsibility** to be honest and punctual. What other rights and responsibilities do you have? List these rights and responsibilities in columns, like this.

Rights	*Responsibilities*
1 Protection of current health and safety legislation	**1** To be honest
2 _____	**2** To be punctual
	3 _____

Discuss your list with other groups of students and your tutor.

Your tutor will have checked that your placement meets the legal requirements of the Health and Safety at Work Act, 1974 and has appropriate insurance cover should you have an accident.

WHAT SHOULD HAPPEN ON PLACEMENT?

One of the objectives of work experience is to allow you to learn, develop and mature by being involved in a work situation. Your age and experience will be two of the issues that will determine how much you learn during this experience. As this may well be your first experience of the work situation, listen to instructions and carry them out to the best of your ability, learn by observation of experienced members of staff and show initiative when basic tasks need doing, such as mopping-up spills, bedmaking, etc.

You should at all times be diplomatic – remember you are a guest of the agency you are now working in. If you are unable to attend the placement, then inform the relevant member of staff in good time.

Show respect towards the staff and clients, but do not be afraid to ask questions or request help if you have any difficulties. You are a student in the placement for only a short time, so behave appropriately towards clients. Keep this in mind when establishing relationships. Be consistent in your relationships with clients, and *earn* the confidence of both clients and staff. Any relationship problems with either clients or staff should be discussed with your tutor or the member of staff in the placement responsible for your supervision.

As you may be on placement for only part of each week, many procedures may not seem logical to you at first. If you are unsure of anything, ask a member of staff or client. Respect the values of the establishment or agency. If you feel unable to discuss something with placement staff, do so with your tutor. Remember that both the tutor and the member of staff responsible for your supervision will be involved in assessing your development and learning whilst on the placement, so trust them and do not be afraid to discuss problems with them.

Aims and objectives of the placement

What work you do while you are on placement will depend on the aims and objectives of that particular establishment or agency. Before you are sent on a particular placement your tutor will have agreed the aims and specific objectives for your placement.

The objectives will include things that you will be expected to do and learn on the placement. A copy of the aims and objectives for each separate placement will be available to you. Discuss them with your tutor and understand them fully before you begin your work-place experience.

The example below illustrates the aims and objectives of a placement in a residential home for the elderly.

The aims are:

- To develop your self-awareness and growth.
- To develop your confidence.
- To provide the opportunity to put theory into practice.
- To familiarise you with the demands of being a member of a team.
- To allow you to observe and study the physical and emotional needs of old people in care.

The objectives (what you should be able to do by the end of the placement) are:

- To demonstrate respect for the dignity and individuality of each old person.
- To encourage each old person to maintain his or her independence.
- To empathise with the residents.
- To understand the individual and group needs of the elderly and attempt to anticipate and meet those needs as appropriate.
- To describe the normal ageing process and some of the common diseases and disabilities affecting the elderly.
- To relate relevant theory to practice.
- To show an understanding of the structure, function and resources used by the establishment.
- To understand and demonstrate the need for 'professionalism' – self-discipline, objectivity, reliability, confidentiality and teamwork.
- To begin to appreciate your own strengths and weaknesses.

A student who performs well on placement manages to achieve the balance of using their initiative, so that they are active and effective, and using their commonsense to know when to check things out with staff.

We all make mistakes

We all make mistakes and there will be times when you feel you should have done something differently. If you are worried about something you have done *do not brood on it* – tell your supervisor or another member of staff. Some days you may be aware that you could be performing much better and this is probably when you are learning the most.

What problems might you come across on your first day at placement?

People who have worked in particular establishments or agencies for any length of time use a language (*jargon*) which those outside that establishment or agency find difficult to understand.

Check out the meanings of the following terms which relate to three possible placements.

Old people's home
- Respite care
- Group living
- EMI
- Reality orientation
- Alzheimer's disease
- Key worker
- Risk taking
- Dementia
- Incontinence
- Diagnosis

School
- Unifix
- Ginn books
- Language skills
- Gender
- AVA room
- Lower-case lettering
- Finger play
- Gender stereotyping

Nursery
- Cultural influences
- Thematic approach
- Interest/theme table
- Vocabulary
- Ethnic group
- Imaginary play
- Psychologist
- Bonding

Write down what these words mean and discuss your answers with colleagues and staff.

RECORDING WHAT YOU DO ON PLACEMENT

You may think that recording and evaluating your placement experience is the last thing that you want to do. However, records are useful to you and your tutor to help you examine situations and your reactions to them so that you can learn from them. The placement record book (or placement diary) should include:

- what you did each day;
- what you found out to help you learn about clients' needs;
- what qualifications and personal qualities are necessary for the job.

A record also helps you develop your skills of investigation, observation and record keeping which are all so important in the caring field.

One way of devising a placement record book is to organise it into three sections:

- **facts** – factual information about the placement;
- **tasks** – what you do in the placement;
- **progress** – how well you carried out tasks and what you learned.

The facts

At first it is important to find out as much as you can about your placement and describe and record this information in a logical way. Find out the placement's location, what the placement does, the numbers of staff and clients, the structure of the organisation and who you are working with. Are there any particular problems or issues you should know about the client group with whom you are working? An example is shown in Figure 8.1.

```
                          Facts

Type of                   Infant school
establishment

Address                   26 King Street,
                          Sheffield

Person in charge          Mr P Johnson

Person responsible        Ms K Smith
for you

Method of travel to       By no. 48 bus
the placement

Journey time              45 minutes

Reporting time            8.45 a.m.

Special clothing          Overalls in class
needs

Etc.
```

▲ *Figure 8.1 Placement facts*

Find out the following about your placement:

- Who is in charge?
- How many staff work there?
- What are their titles?
- What are their main jobs and responsibilities?
- What qualifications do they have?
- What personal qualities (for example, patience, stamina, understanding, pleasant personality) are necessary for their jobs?

When you have answered these questions then finding your way about may become a little easier and you will become more active and secure in the placement. Knowing what jobs or roles people have also helps. All this information should be in the facts section of your record.

ACTIVITY

Use the following headings to create a fact record for **your** placement.

```
1  What is the full name, address and
   telephone number of your placement?

   Name       _____

   Address    _____

              _____

   Tel. no.   _____
```

2   What type of placement is it, e.g.
    nursery, school, day centre, etc.?

    _____

3   How do you propose to travel to the
    placement?
    Walking
    Bus
    Tube
    Train
    Car
    Bike
    Other

4   Using a local map list brief directions
    from home to the placement.

5   How long will your journey take?

    a) in rush hour _____

    b) in off-peak times _____

6   What time do you report to your
    placement? _____

7   What time will you need to set your
    alarm clock? _____

8   What tasks will you need to carry out
    before leaving home each day for the
    placement?
    Bath - shower - press clothes - pack
    overalls - clean shoes - make breakfast
    - prepare packed lunch - others.

9   How much time altogether will you need
    to carry out these tasks? _____

10 What time will you leave home to arrive
    on time? _____

11 What is the name and job title of the
    person you are to report to?

    Name _____

    Job title _____

Note taking

While on placement you should find out, observe and make notes on the
following:

The organisation and function of the placement
- When and why was it built?
- How many people use the service?
- What is the purpose of the service?
- How much does it cost the user?

Does the service meet the users' needs?
- What tasks are carried out to meet the users' physical needs?
- What tasks are carried out to meet the users' psychological needs?
- What tasks are carried out to meet the users' medical needs?
- What tasks are carried out to meet the users' social needs?
- Are there any users' needs not being met – if so what are they?

Has the service links with the local community?
- Identify the links, if any, that the service has with the community. Some possible ones are shown in Figure 8.2.

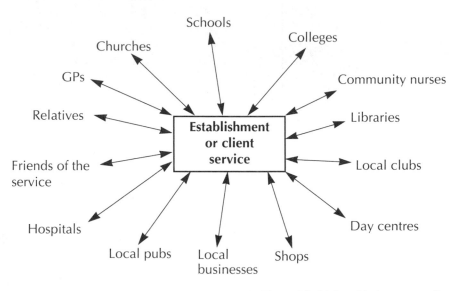

▲ *Figure 8.2 Links with the community*

Always take a notebook and pen with you to make notes as often as you can without disrupting the routine of the establishment. Break-times are appropriate periods in which to record things and ask staff questions. Do not record any client's or staff member's name. Write up your record book regularly and at least at the end of every placement day.

Confidentiality

Remember, confidentiality is of the greatest importance. You have no right to intrude into clients' lives. In your placement you are likely to obtain information about clients. Any information, of whatever nature, *must* remain confidential to you and the appropriate staff in the placement. You may wish to use situations you have experienced or observed in your placement to illustrate your record or assignment. If you do this make sure that you maintain the confidentiality of the client and the staff you work with. Always write up your placement record so that neither clients nor staff can be recognised from the information you record.

TASKS

What do you write in the tasks section of your placement record? As you become more sure of yourself and get to know the staff and clients you will be allocated simple tasks to carry out on your own. If you are working in a school you may take a small group of children for a craft activity or perhaps read them a story. What you did, how you organised the situation and how the children reacted should all be recorded in the tasks section.

Figure 8.3 shows part of a task record written by a student.

I felt very happy today about going to my placement.

I began work by helping M*** (a care assistant) dress Mrs J*** who is 90 years old. Mrs J*** is very confused but this morning she was co-operative. I put her dress on. I think she is very frustrated at not being able to help herself – she nearly hit me.

I made the bed in Mrs J*** room and disposed of the incopads and replaced them with fresh ones. I made some more beds and M*** showed me where the bedding was kept as I needed clean sheets and some draw sheets.

This placement is really good, you can sit down and talk to the residents and staff as long as you complete your tasks.

After break M*** showed me how to clean the toilets and sinks properly using bleach and hot water. She also explained what protective clothing to wear, such as gloves and apron.

At dinner time I helped the rest of the staff and some of the residents to lay the tables. I then helped some of the residents to sit down. After dinner I hoovered the bedrooms. I was allowed to go home at 3.30 p.m.

I really enjoyed today, I got on well with staff and enjoyed the work. I also enjoyed helping to dress some of the residents even though one of them nearly hit me.

▲ *Figure 8.3 Task record*

Observations to be made during your placement

- What were your first impressions of the placement? Write about how you felt and what you liked and disliked about your first day.
- Draw a plan of the placement and list all the staff and the kind of work they do.
- How many rooms are there? What activities take place in each room? Which residents sit in which room?
- Make a list of the tasks you carried out and the duties that will be expected of you during your stay.
- Put the following information in the tasks section of your record each day: work and activities undertaken – your observations.

- Meals – At what times are meals served? Describe a menu for one day. What special diets do any of the residents have?
- Social activities – What activities do the residents take part in? Do they organise these themselves or do the staff do so? When do these activities take place?

Recording may seem tedious, but it gives you and your tutor a chance to stand back and reflect. You should use the experience as a positive step in your learning. It is also an important part of the placement assessment process which we shall discuss later.

You now have some idea as to what you record in the *facts* and *tasks* sections of your record. One other very important aspect left to discuss is the *progress* section.

PROGRESS

In this section of your record you should record your feelings about the work you did and what you have learned from your experiences. Do this every day and it will be much easier to analyse what you have learned at the end of the placement by referring back to your daily record.

At first, you may feel that you did not do as well as you expected in your placement. Did you have the personal qualities and the necessary skills? If not, have you the ability or aptitude to learn these skills? Try to record why you thought it did not go so well, what improvements you would make next time, what you learned from the exercise and what you need to discuss with your tutor.

Are your feelings and attitudes about the clients, placement or staff the same now as they were on your first day? Give examples of how your feelings towards the clients or users of the service have changed and why.

ACTIVITY

Write about your experiences by answering the following questions:

1 What did you learn about yourself?

2 What did you learn about dealing with people?

3 What event or task did you find particularly satisfying?

4 What event or task did you find particularly difficult?

5 Write about why you felt the way you did in those situations.

6 What would you do differently if you had the chance to experience these situations again and why?

ACTIVITY

Choose one positive experience you had on placement – an experience that left you feeling happy, pleased or satisfied. Record the details and compare them with a negative incident – one which left you feeling angry, frustrated or fed up. Select a partner in the class and tell them of your experiences. Discuss both your own experiences and theirs. Then write down what you have both learned from these experiences.

The experiences you choose to discuss can be very simple. For example one student wrote:

```
I found it particularly satisfying to take
the tea and coffee to the residents because
most of them really appreciate it and look
forward to it. You feel that you are doing
something useful. It also gave me a chance
to meet and talk to the residents.
   I found it particularly difficult at first
to empty and clean commodes and to clean
residents after they had been incontinent.
As I got to know the residents this part of
the job got easier.
```

This exercise will help you to learn more about your experiences and will enable a second person to express an opinion on what happened. It will show you that from every situation, negative or positive, you can learn from your experiences. By discussing the situations and your feelings with a second person you will become aware of your attitude and feelings.

ASSESSMENT

During your placement you will be visited regularly by your school or college tutor who will observe you working with clients. Your tutor will be concerned with seeing how well you put into practice the skills that you have learned at college.

Work-based assessment is an important feature of all social care courses. Whilst you are on placement your skills in working with and helping clients will be assessed. This is usually done by you, your college tutor and the agency or organisation member of staff responsible for you whilst you are there.

Reports

Any report written by the placement staff will be discussed with you and you will have an opportunity to comment and discuss the contents with the writer. The report plays a vital part in your self-development and can be used by you to increase your level of self-awareness. The assessment report will enable your tutors to identify and discuss with you your weaknesses and strengths, and help you plan improvement. The report is also a written record of how well you have done on the placement and can be used, if you want, as a type of reference when you are looking for employment.

Competences

In what kinds of situations and behaviour will the college and agency staff be assessing you? Since 1986, the National Council for Vocational Qualifications (NCVQ) have identified certain tasks (competences) which staff and students in the work place are expected to carry out according to their level of responsibilities. Tasks that you are expected to do, for example, bedmaking, are called *competences* and during your placement you will be assessed in how skilled you are in carrying out some of these competences, by the college and agency staff.

Example of a competence – assist client with grooming

This competence or task has a number of different sections or elements. For example:

- remove surplus hair (shaving, trim beards, body hair);
- hair care;
- cut nails;
- maintain clothing and shoes;
- help clients with dressing and undressing.

When you can do all of these tasks well you will be competent in these jobs.

Let us look at the stages you have to do to cut a client's nails:

- assemble all the essential equipment;
- use the equipment correctly;
- examine toe and finger nails;
- record and report accurately the condition of the client's nails;
- ensure finger-nails are brushed clean;
- aim to minimise any discomfort to the client.

▲ *Cutting a client's nails*   © *Tony Othen, courtesy of Age Concern, England*

Assessment of a competence

Your tutor and supervisor in the placement will not only be looking at the end result, for example, how well you changed an incontinent elderly person in bed, but they will also be looking at how you carried out the job.

They will be looking for evidence that you respected the elderly person by taking into account their privacy and kept their confidentiality. Also if you encouraged them to maintain their self-respect and took into consideration their age, sex, physical and mental condition. Did you encourage the client to be as independent as possible? Did you use language suitable and understandable, taking into account the client's culture, race and religion?

You can now see that just washing a client's face or bathing him or her is not enough. How you do it is just as important.

Other things staff will wish to discuss with you will be your planning and organisational ability. These include:

- how you gathered information;
- your observation skills;
- how you use equipment;
- your ability to get on with clients and other members of staff;

Do you listen and can you communicate with clients, staff and the public?

A FINAL NOTE

Your placement experience is as important as your work at college. Remember that you are being educated and trained to work for and serve dependent people who are vulnerable. One day it could be you or someone you love who is the client, so try always to treat people as you would wish to be treated yourself. Good luck!

ASSIGNMENT 7

The following assignment will allow you to use all the material discussed in this chapter. Read Chapter 7 before attempting this assignment.

Investigating the needs of children with a handicap in the community
This assignment is to investigate the needs of a specific client group and how these needs are being met within your local community. Working in small groups, each of you will need to look at a particular aspect and produce a report on it. You will then need to share your findings with the rest of your group and plan a group presentation to the class.

Aims of the assignment
- To investigate the physical, social, emotional and intellectual needs of children who are handicapped.
- To investigate the national provision that exists to meet the needs of the client group you have selected.
- To investigate and evaluate the services that are available to meet the needs of your chosen client group in your local community.
- To give you opportunities for group and individual investigation.
- To enable you to incorporate skills and experience developed in work placement with children.

Objectives of the assignment
- As a group, collect data by a variety of sampling techniques. Then tabulate and summarise the data, and display it graphically.
- Explore the services provided in your local community and the social and economic factors influencing their provision.

- Recognise that the community consists of sub-groups with different problems and needs.
- Survey local provision in the community for children with a handicap.
- Relate local services to national provision.

The skills that you will use and develop are listed below. Discuss them with your tutor and classmates before you begin the assignment.

Skills	How you will use and develop them
Managing and developing self	Plan tasks in terms of what you need to find out. Plan time effectively and meet deadlines. Compare others' ideas with your own.
Working with and relating to others	Contribute your own ideas about how the tasks are to be completed by the group. Negotiate and undertake tasks as part of a team. Give and accept support, help and criticism to and from others.
Communicating	Communicate orally in both group and class. Select appropriate forms of communication for each task. Present your findings effectively in your own written report.
Managing tasks and solving problems	Set up an action plan and evaluate its feasibility. Review the action plan and monitor your progress in carrying it out. If necessary, take appropriate action to modify the plan.
Numeracy	Use appropriate numerical skills.
Planning tasks and data, and solving problems	Decide how you will collect information and organise and review information and data. Draw conclusions, evaluate and discuss them.

Assessment

You will be assessed:
- as a group, on your planning and achievement of the aims of the investigation. This will be based on a group action plan and preparation for a group presentation to the class;
- on how you contribute to the work of the group. This will be based on evaluations from your tutor, other students and yourself;
- on your own research and ideas, and on your presentation of these in your individual report.

Group action plan

What you hope to find out:

_____

_____

_____

_____

Allocation of various tasks to be investigated in the group.

Task	Who is responsible	How you are going to carry out tasks	Timescale

Presentation plan
Description of the main findings you will present.

_____

_____

_____

_____

How you will present your findings.

_____

_____

_____

_____

Materials, charts, etc. to be used.

_____

_____

_____

_____

Allocation of tasks in the group.

_____

_____

_____

_____

Index